Arizona

Disaster

The Hassayampa Story
1886–2009

Jim Liggett

The Hassayampa River downstream of the Walnut Grove Dam site

Water, water, water...There is no shortage of water in the desert but exactly the right amount, a perfect ratio of water to rock. Of water to sand, insuring that wide, free, open, generous spacing among plants and animals, homes and towns and cities, which makes the arid West so different from any other part of the nation. There is no lack of water here unless you try to establish a city where no city should be.

Edward Abbey, Wilderness Reader

The picture on the cover is a photo of a diorama in the Desert Caballeros Western Museum in Wickenburg, Arizona, done by George Fuller of Wickenburg. It is the artist's depiction of the flood wave from the Walnut Grove Dam failure exiting Box Canyon. Photograph of the diorama is courtesy of the Desert Caballeros Western Museum.

Back cover: The Hassayampa River Preserve is a virtual desert oasis. The green trees—mostly cottonwoods, willows, and mesquites but also palms and other vegetation—are a result of the constant supply of water. Water appears on the surface here throughout the year as shown in the inset taken after a summer of very low precipitation.

Library of Congress Control Number: 2009938080

Paperback ISBN: 978-1-7344884-2-5

E-Book ISBN: 978-1-7344884-3-2

DESERT ROAMER
——PRESS——

Cheyenne, Wyoming

To Carole

Table of contents

Preface

On May 31, 1889, the South Fork Dam, 14 miles upstream of Johnstown, Pennsylvania, collapsed. The result was the worst flood disaster in the United States to date (2008) with more than 2200 people killed. The dam was 72 feet high and Lake Conemaugh held 4.8 billion gallons of water.

On February 22, 1890, the Walnut Grove Dam (see map) in central Arizona collapsed. It was 110 feet high and held 9.8 billion gallons of water. Only the fact of a low population density downstream of the dam prevented the death toll from reaching that of the South Fork Dam.

The immediate cause of both disasters was the same, an inadequate spillway to carry off flood water. Aside from the spillway, poor engineering and poor construction may have been contributory causes in both cases. In both cases economics, and the resulting constraints imposed by owners, limited the engineer's ability to make the dams safe.

The Johnstown flood was a signature event in Pennsylvania history, but the Walnut Grove failure is barely mentioned, if at all, in Arizona history books. The latter, however, made an impact in the Territory. Many of the famous—Brodie, Wittmann, O'Neill, Powell—played roles either before or after the flood. The flood may have prevented Wickenburg from becoming the Territorial capital. It caused the greatest loss of life of any single event in Arizona to this date with the exception of the collision of two airliners over the Grand Canyon in 1956. Although a disaster, the failure of the dam prevented the sort of destruction due to hydraulic mining on the Hassayampa River, Weaver Creek and Antelope Creek that befell several rivers in California.

The upper Hassayampa River.

The late 19th century and early 20th century was a period of innovation and outstanding engineering feats in the United States. Much of the infrastructure—bridges, tall buildings, dams, irrigation systems, water distribution systems, sewage systems, the railroad network, many highways—were designed and constructed by outstanding engineers. Against that background comes some engineering failures, including the South Fork Dam and the Walnut Grove Dam. Failures, especially dam failures, cause death and destruction—a high price to pay for the lessons learned.

This book is about more than the Walnut Grove Dam failure; it is the story of the Hassayampa River from the late nineteenth century to modern times. The flood that occurred after the dam failure was the primary event, but the story concerns the riches in the watershed, floods subsequent to 1890, attempts at damming the river, a bit on the ecology of the river, and environmental concerns.

The latter involve mining in general and especially hydraulic mining, which was to be the purpose of the Walnut Grove Dam. Because hydraulic mining did not occur on a large scale in Arizona, examples are brought in from California to show what could have been the fate of the Hassayampa.

The facts

Senator Hiram Johnson[1] said, "The first casualty when war comes is the truth." He might have included disasters as well. In such an event the public is hungry for knowledge. Rumors, often printed in newspapers, fulfill a craving to know what happened, and facts are not sufficiently checked afterward. One author in writing about the Walnut Grove disaster aptly said: "... [newspapers] gave rather contradictory accounts ..." Articles about the disaster still appear from time to time. Although they serve to inform, "facts" are often garnered from unreliable newspaper accounts or, as nearly as I can determine, invented. I have a file labeled "Misc

---

1. Governor of California 1911-1917, senator 1917-1945. The quote comes from his first speech in the Senate in 1917.

garbage" from which can be read such nonsense as "Wickenburg was destroyed, every building falling before the awful assault."

I thought that the engineering literature would be reliable, but it is not free of conflicts and contradictions, even in the critical dimensions of the dam that should have been known to some precision. And engineers are not above pointing the finger of blame at someone else and away from themselves. One of the purposes of this book is to gather information and present the best knowledge available from this distance in time. In doing so, I occasionally quote sources that have presented, in my opinion, false "facts." I do so not to criticize the sources but to inform the reader that I am aware of alternate information and have considered its veracity. Of course, there are a number of accounts that I cannot verify and some conflicting statements where the truth is unknown; I try to identify these situations.

The record is especially conflicted in the number of lives lost in the flood. Published numbers range from a low of 10 (many more bodies than 10 were recovered) to a high of 150[2]. After reading the published accounts, I would *guess at* 70 plus or minus 20. In newspaper articles and the engineering literature, there appear numbers of total deaths that *seem* to be authoritative and definite (e.g., that of Moritz (1948, p. 3) which gives 129); I do not believe any of them.

In spite of the above paragraph, I am compelled to give my own unsubstantiated interpretation of facts and events in many locations. I identify such instances so that the reader can use his/her own judgment on how much credence to give to my opinion.

---

2. Perhaps the latter figure came from Walker (1975, p. 79): "One mining camp known to have a population of 150 miners and their families disappeared in the mile-wide torrent as it rushed down to the town of Wickenburg, where it spread out in the mesquite thickets." I have no idea what he was talking about.

Finding information on the Walnut Grove Dam failure is simple on one hand, the best paper and a landmark study being that of Dill (1987). Although Dill was diligent in seeking a great many accounts and meticulously documenting his sources, he occasionally misstates facts, and he explains little of the numerical details involved in the design, construction, and failure. I hope that this short book overcomes those deficiencies.

Finally, although the Walnut Grove Dam disaster was an epic event in territorial Arizona, it gets surprisingly little notice in the books on Arizona history. I would like the citizens of Arizona to know about this interesting part of their heritage, an event that changed a part of the state forever.

Acknowledgements

Many people deserve thanks for helping me put together this book.

Joe Stevens' assistance was invaluable. He is a local historian in Wickenburg and he wrote much of the first chapter. Joe accompanied me on all of the trips along the Hassayampa River: the Walnut Grove Dam site, the Lower dam site and the flume line below the Lower dam, the latter two over primitive roads in his ATV. His knowledge of local geography, trails and people are outstanding. He read progressive versions the manuscript and has provided valuable correction and criticism.

Pieter Bruggraaf pointed out facts in the names of Pauline Weaver and the Hassayampa River.

Christopher Magirl of the U.S. Geological Survey in Tucson (now with the USGS in Tacoma, Washington) pointed me toward resources from the USGS and elsewhere, including stream flow records and the book by Webb, et al. (2007). In many cases he provided me with the relevant pages from various publications.

Chris read the manuscript, making corrections or suggestions in the English, the general presentation and technical details.

Charles Herner, a historian living in Tucson, is author of *The Arizona Rough Riders* and has recently completed a biography of Alexander O. Brodie. He has given several lectures on the Walnut Grove Dam failure. We exchanged considerable information. Charlie read the penultimate version of the manuscript and made many suggestions

Librarians and archivists of several institutions have gone out of their way to search for materials. Deserving special mention are: Rachel Anne Inbar and Jill Powell of the Engineering Library at Cornell University; Jeff Diver, Virginia Cole, Amy Blumenthal and Fred Muratori of the Cornell libraries; Nancy Sawyer, Archivist at the Arizona State Libraries, Archives and Public Records; Coi E. Drummond-Gehrig at the Denver Public Library; and the staff and archivists at Sharlot Hall Museum in Prescott. The staff of the Arizona Historical Society Museum in Tucson—and especially Jim Turner, historian—were particularly helpful in providing newspapers, the letters of Dr. Genung, the diaries of Prof. Blake and many other items.

Just when I thought that I was almost finished, I got a call from Marsha Swirsky and Mary Dodd, who were taking a paralegal class at Yavapai College in Prescott. Their class was about to hold a mock trial of *Wickenburg, et al. v. the Walnut Grove Water Storage Company*. I sent them the manuscript. They then visited the Arizona State Libraries, Archives and Public Records and found some material that I had not previously seen. Appendix IV, the plans and specifications for the dam, is a result as is the material in the Litigation section that refers to Appendix IV. Also, the judge's instructions to the jury come from a disk that they prepared.

Last, but certainly not least, Carole, my wife, was a great help in many aspects. Her perceptive questions often kept me on the correct path.

About the author

Jim Liggett was born in Los Angeles, California, but immigrated to Arizona when he was six years old—as soon as he could convince his parents that Arizona was a better place. He went through elementary school in Glendale and high school in Prescott. Jim attended Texas Technological College (now Texas Tech University) in Lubbock then Stanford University where he received his masters and Ph.D. degrees in engineering.

After short employments at Chance Vought Aircraft in Dallas and the University of Wisconsin, Jim joined the faculty of Cornell University where he remained for 35 years. Although the demands of a career had taken him far from Arizona, he returned upon retirement, settling in Wickenburg as both Glendale and Prescott had long since outgrown the small-town atmosphere that he enjoyed.

Jim was introduced to the Walnut Grove Dam while working on the book *Desert Hiking out Wickenburg Way* by Dana Burden. Climbing around the scant remains at the dam site and reading about the failure brought up some engineering questions that needed answers. An attempt to obtain answers often brought up more questions and major contradictions in what had been written about the dam. This book is an attempt to enhance and correct the record of the events of 1890 and the subsequent attempts at constructing a dam on the Hassayampa River. It is also an attempt to fill in a gap in the territorial history of Arizona since this major and defining event is largely ignored in the history books.

CHAPTER 1: GOLD

Thomas H. Brown and Thomas B. Hunt stood on the east hillside from the Walnut Grove Dam watching as the water cascading over the rockfill structure became deeper. Assistant Superintendent Brown already feared for the integrity of the dam to such an extent that he had sent Dan Burke downstream to warn that a flood was coming. The noise of the spillway, immediately adjacent to the dam on the west side, and the water overtopping the dam and cascading 110 feet down the downstream face was deafening. Spray enveloped everything in the vicinity.

As they sat transfixed by the impending disaster, the entire dam appeared to move downstream, pushed by the mighty force of the overfilled lake. The noise increased as rocks collided with one another. Then the dam simply disappeared as though it had sunk into the earth. A wall of water proceeded down the Hassayampa River sweeping everything it could reach.

In terms of lives lost, it was the worst natural disaster to hit Arizona to this date (2009)[1]; the death toll from a single event was

---

1. However, the National Weather Service states (http://www.wrh.noaa.gov/ fgz/ science/flashfld.php?wfo=fgz): "The loss of 23 lives and the devastation which occurred during the Labor Day weekend of September 5-6, 1970, make this [flood] event the greatest natural disaster in the history of the state." Perhaps one can quibble about the definition of the word "natural" or perhaps the 1890 disaster didn't count because Arizona was a territory at the time.

exceeded only by the collision of two airliners over the Grand Canyon in 1956. A smaller dam, some 12 miles downstream, was swept away together with its construction camp, the town of Wickenburg was flooded (some say to a depth of 40 feet, but see the depth hydrograph, Figure 4-1), valuable farmland was destroyed never to be restored, the rock-crushing arrastras[2] along the river disappeared into the swift water, and the town of Seymour was lost and never rebuilt.

The Gold Rush

The Walnut Grove Dam was an important chapter in the search for gold in the American West and, especially, the Arizona Territory. The first chapter began with the 49ers. In January of 1848 gold was discovered in California. The result was a stampede of people, called the 49ers, from the east to the west. Many took ships around South America, arriving in San Francisco Bay. Others came across the country by the much-glorified Conestoga Wagon, while others simply traveled by horseback or on foot. Some of those heading west traveled via the Santa Fe trail. From Santa Fe, Territory of New Mexico, they turned south to southern New Mexico and south of the Chiricahua Mountains, located in present-day southeastern Arizona. From southeastern Arizona the pioneers turned north down the San Pedro River then across country to the small Mexican town of Tucson. Tucson was to become a part of the New Mexico Territory in 1853 with the Gadsden Purchase, acquisition of land

---

2. An arrastra was a circular device for crushing ore-bearing rock. It consisted of a pole in the center of a circle, an arm extending outward from the pole and large rocks attached to the arm by ropes. The arm was dragged along by a horse or mule so the rocks slid on the ground. The ore was placed on the ground so that it was ground up by action of the rocks.

south of the Gila River to the present border with Mexico. In 1846 this route had been established by the Mormon Battalion, headed by then Lt. Col. Crook and guided by Pauline[3] Weaver. Both of these individuals would have major impacts during later years in central Arizona. From Tucson the 49ers would head northwest along the Santa Cruz River to its confluence with the Gila—along the Anza Trail[4]. In this location the friendly Pima and Maricopa Indians had supplies of wheat as well as the "three sisters"—corn, beans, and squash. These food supplies were vital to the travelers. The route was dry and barren, causing great hardship on travelers and their animals.

Upon departing the Pima and Maricopa villages, the early gold seekers proceeded westward along the Gila River to Yuma Crossing, a ferry across the Colorado River. While in the early 1800s there had been mountain men in central Arizona, none of the 49ers headed north into central Arizona. The lure of California gold and the fear of the dreaded Apache Indians kept them moving west.

By the early 1860s, most of the California gold seekers had not made their fortunes and were growing restless. Pauline Weaver, during the winter of 1861-62, found gold along the Colorado River and the town of La Paz was founded. Some of the 49ers

---

3. His real name was Powell Weaver. "... his name was later given as Powleen, Pawleen, Pawlino, Paolino, Paul, and Pauline" (*Days Past*, Sharlot Hall Museum, Nov. 26, 2000). A Spanish name was, apparently, Paulino or Paolino, which is sometime shortened to Paolín, pronounced (almost) as the English "Pauline." Pauline is used most commonly in the literature; thus, I have used it here even though it is wrong. (See Byrkit and Hooper, 1993)

4. The Anza trail is named for Juan Bautista de Anza who was a military man for New Spain. It is the route followed in 1774-1776 by the Spanish Expedition, about 30 families on a trek to present-day San Francisco. These pioneers founded several missions en route.

headed east, moving from one muddy well to another through harsh conditions. The area around the current town of Bouse became known as Weaver Mining District #1.

Eighteen-sixty-three was a banner year. The Arizona Territory was created by Congress on February 24 and formally organized on December 29. Two major gold discoveries were made in the Hassayampa watershed: The Vulture Mine south of Wickenburg and Rich Hill north of Wickenburg. Gold was also discovered at Lynx Creek—which is not in the Hassayampa watershed—south of Prescott. Two of the famous mountain men of the West converged on Prescott. The Town of Wickenburg was founded. Prescott became the territorial capital of Arizona (1864-1867 and again from 1877-1889).

In 1863 the two mountain men—gold seekers, guides, trappers, and explorers—Joseph Rutherford Walker[5] and Pauline Weaver, opened central Arizona to the white man. Walker had crossed and crisscrossed the Rocky Mountains and Sierras many times; indeed his life story, recounted by Gilbert (1983) in his book, *Westering Man*, is an amazing story of survival. He was 65 years old in 1863 with failing eyesight and his last major exploration and adventure was in Arizona. Though he was little interested in gold—he did not take part in the California gold rush according to Gilbert—he led a group of men in search of gold from California, through southern Utah and into Colorado. Since many in his party were Confederate sympathizers, Walker wanted to avoid trouble with Union troops. He turned south into New Mexico in

---

5. Much of the literature, including Connor's book, cited below, uses Reddeford for Walker's middle name. Gilbert (1983, pp. 7 and 299) makes a convincing case that his name was Rutherford.

late summer of 1862. In northern New Mexico, Daniel Ellis Conner, a southerner on the run from Union troops, joined the Walker party. Conner was a prolific diarist and wrote detailed descriptions of Walker's further adventures, which appear in Conner's book (1956) and were used by Gilbert.

Walker's goal was central Arizona, but he was delayed for three months in New Mexico fighting a running battle with the Indians led by Mangas Coloradas, a fierce chief. (Mangas was captured by deception, turned over to Union forces and, in a shameful manner, killed.) From New Mexico Walker proceeded to southeastern Arizona where he followed the pioneer trail to the Gila River and village of the PimaMaricopa Indians.

Walker traveled along the Gila River to the Hassayampa and turned north up the Hassayampa where they met a group of Indians and their chief, Irotaba. Gilbert (1983) calls them Tonto-Apaches. Connor calls them "Apache-mohaves," but the editors' footnote in Connor's book states: "These Indians are correctly called the Yavapai..." Gilbert does have the word "Yavapai" in his book. Gilbert reports: "Not far from the present town of Wickenburg, at a good campsite where there was water in the intermittent Hassayampa, Irotaba said [that] he wanted to halt and parley." That campsite was probably at the future location of Brill's farm and the Hassayampa River Preserve (see map in Preface), a location near Wickenburg where the Hassayampa flows on the surface year-round. Another location with constant surface water, north of Wickenburg, is Box Canyon—not mentioned by Gilbert—but Walker would probably not take his men into Box Canyon as that would be a prime spot for an Indian ambush, shooting from atop the canyon walls. However, Connor does mention "the 'big cañon' in the Haviamp" through which the party passed. Connor (1956, p. 95) said that later the party camped at "one of the prettiest points in Arizona and has since retained the name we gave it and still goes by the name of Walnutgrove."

Probably Walker and his men were the first of European origin to visit the oasis south of present-day Wickenburg and the site of the Walnut Grove Dam. Although, in the early 1800s there had been mountain men in central Arizona, and Walker in 1861 had been 100 miles north of Prescott (Gilbert, 1983, p. 269).

Walker proceeded on to near the origin of the Hassayampa and set up a permanent camp, discovered gold and made mining claims. They were in need of supplies and the nearest source was the Pima-Maricopa Indian settlements. In June of 1863 Walker's group left for a 20-day round trip to Maricopa Wells.

Meanwhile, a group of three men, known as the Peeples' party after Abraham Peeples, their leader, arrived in Yuma. These men wanted to go into central Arizona to prospect for gold. They found Pauline Weaver in town and asked him to be their guide. Weaver agreed but stated that they needed a larger group. In the end ten men departed Yuma Crossing. Both the timing and the route that they took are uncertain.

Some accounts say that they headed north along the Colorado River. Once in the area south of present-day Parker, the party left the river and proceeded in a northeasterly direction to intersect the Bill Williams River. They continued along Date Creek to the low mountains northwest of present-day Wickenburg. They followed along the base of these mountains to the east and found rich placer deposits in Antelope Creek and Indian Creek (now called Weaver Creek). Large nuggets of gold were found on top of the mountain between these creeks at Rich Hill. In addition to the placers, a hard rock mine was established.

Conner (1956, p. 104) implies that Weaver reached the gold fields by another route. He reports that after the Walker party departed Maricopa Wells, Weaver was seen "coming up the Gila river." Weaver was told about the gold discovery and then continued to the Pima settlement. Afterward the Weaver party "... immediately returned to our trail as far as the mountains and began to prospect on their own hook, forty or fifty miles southwest of our woods." Connor mentions nothing of Rich Hill or of Weaver finding gold. Gilbert (p.270) confirms that route (although he used Connor's notes): "From there [Fort Yuma] they [Weaver] went to the Pima villages and then also turned up the Hassayampa. Exactly three weeks after Walker's prospectors had made their strike along streams of Spruce Ridge [Lynx Creek, primarily], Weaver's group arrived in the vicinity of what is now Wickenburg, fifty miles to the southeast, and found gold in paying quantities." Gilbert does not mention Rich Hill.

Weaver did reach Prescott and is sometimes called "the first citizen of Prescott." The above accounts imply that he was later than Walker, but Trimble (2004) states: "Weaver moved north the next year ('63) and was already camped on Granite Creek, the future site of Prescott, when the Walker party arrived." Connor's failure to mention that Weaver was in Prescott implies that he was not, and it's hardly conceivable that Weaver could have been at Prescott and Walker not knowing about his presence. Whatever the sequence of events, Weaver and Walker made some of the most important gold discoveries in the state and opened central Arizona to the gold seekers, which quickly led to Prescott becoming the territorial capital.

Rich Hill was one of two discoveries that fueled the gold rush in central Arizona. In 1863 Henry Wickenburg discovered gold just west of the Hassayampa River and established the Vulture Mine (see map in Preface), one of the richest finds in Arizona. Wickenburg was born in 1819 in Essen-Holsterhausen, Germany, under the name Johannes Heinricus Wickenburg (Bansner, 2006)[6]. He reportedly came to the United States to avoid prosecution for illegally mining coal on his own property with the mine entrance hidden in his barn; however, the top layer of coal in the area is at a depth of 130 meters (427 ft), probably too deep for a casual mining operation.

Figure 1-1. Henry Wickenburg

---

6. Many publications have Wickenburg's name as Heinrich Heintzel (e.g., *The Arizona Republic*, Oct. 28, 2007, p. T8; Corle, 1951). Although Bansner (2006) has looked up Wickenburg's baptismal certificate, there remains a question as to his birth name.

The ore from the Vulture Mine was processed in arrastras built along the Hassayampa River, which at that time apparently had more surface flow than it does now. Henry established a small ranch on the bank of the Hassayampa where he farmed the rich topsoil along the river. By the 1870s the area's population was said to be about 20,000—mostly men—between the towns of Wickenburg and Prescott. Arizona now had proven gold fields and the upper Hassayampa basin was shown to be one of the most mineral-rich areas in the world.

North of Rich Hill was a beautiful valley complete with streams and walnut trees. A part of this valley was settled by Abraham Peeples and the entire valley became known as Peeples Valley. To the east was another beautiful valley along the Hassayampa River where the town of Walnut Grove was settled. Both areas were great for cattle raising and farming. Just down the river from the town of Walnut Grove, the Hassayampa passes through a constricted area between canyon walls, a perfect place to construct a dam.

The Bates brothers

Wells H. Bates, 35, and DeWitt C. Bates, 38, attempted to take advantage of the Arizona gold in 1881. The brothers were sons of a New York lawyer and Wells was a lawyer. DeWitt was variously listed as a lawyer's clerk or stockbroker. They bought a gold mine west of Rich Hill. In 1883 they became interested in the placer deposits downstream of Rich Hill—primarily in Antelope Creek and Weaver Creek—for hydraulic mining[7] (Dill, 1987, p. 284), which requires an enormous quantity of water. The only reliable water source was the Hassayampa River. They filed claims for

---

7. Chapter 3 (page 21) explains hydraulic mining in detail.

placer mining rights and for all the water in the river. For a dam site they chose a location south of Walnut Grove on Judge Abner Wade's ranch where the river passes from a broad valley into the Hassayampa River Canyon, now designated a wilderness area (see map in Preface). After claiming a huge area for mining purposes as well as all the water in Hassayampa, the brothers departed for New York seeking financial backing. Apparently, their quest for New York gold proved very frustrating as everyone "knew" that the rainfall in arid Arizona was insufficient to fill a reservoir. They eventually persuaded financiers Charles H. Dillingham and J. N. Newberry to finance a stock offering. Dillingham and Newberry then enlisted the help of the eminent geologist, William P. Blake (see page 47 for material about Blake).

Blake and Wells Bates traveled to the placer area where, after a few days of exploring and gold panning, Blake pronounced the area sufficiently rich to justify the cost of a dam and transmission flumes to supply water for hydraulic mining. Wells Bates then contacted Abner Wade and acquired the rights to construct a 60-foot high dam (Dill, 1987, p. 288)[8].

In New York the financiers formed two companies, the Walnut Grove Water Storage Company and the Piedmont Cattle Company[9], both incorporated in Kentucky. Although the primary

---

8. The actual dam was 110 feet high, the highest in the United States at that time. The English Dam in California had a height of 100 feet, but it was 131 feet above the lowest point of the foundation. It failed in 1883, before the construction of the Walnut Grove Dam.

9. An article ("Description of the Piedmont Stock Range in Maricopa, Yavapai and Yuma Counties, Arizona Territory"), apparently written by William P. Blake and circulated by Dillingham and Newberry in 1886, describes cattle raising and the profits to be made by such an enterprise in glowing terms. It is available at http://digitalcommons.library.arizona.edu/.

purpose of the dam was hydraulic mining, irrigation would ensure its success. An agreement between the two companies would allow Piedmont to take 100 miner's inches (see footnote on page 68) of water, about 2.7 cubic feet per second (1212 gallons per minute). Wells Bates received $100,000 and became a director of the two companies in return for his placer claims (Dill, 1987, p. 288).

Wells Bates would remain with the project until failure.

Henry Spingler Van Beuren[10]

In 1888 Dillingham ceded the presidency of the Walnut Grove Water Storage Company to Henry S. Van Beuren, who had bought J. N. Newberry's interest in the company. Van Beuren's ancestors owned a large farm in Manhattan in the vicinity of present-day Broadway and Fourteenth Street. The urbanization of New York made the property enormously valuable, providing the Van Beurens with nearly a million dollars per year in rent (*New York Times*, Oct. 15, 1983, p. 10). Van Beuren was elected director of the Company on June 4, 1886 (Anon., 1936). Apparently, Van Beuren took a personal interest in the project. He traveled to Arizona and set up camp with his niece, coachman and niece's maid near the Lower dam site. He was responsible for hiring Alexander O. Brodie (see page 55) as chief engineer and superintendent.

---

10. Van Beuren is sometime misspelled as "Van Buren." According to an article in the *Wickenburg Sun* (July 21, 1961; reprinted Oct. 2, 1969), "... Van Buren [was] a relative of Martin Van Buren, president of the United States from 1837 to 1841..." This article is the only one that I have seen that linked Van Beuren to the president. It has spelled his name incorrectly; the correct spelling appears on letters, court documents, legal papers and other materials. He is not related to the president.

The Van Beuren ties with Arizona would continue long into the future. Henry's niece, Mary Hanlon (see page 37), married Brodie and became first lady of the Arizona Territory when Brodie was appointed governor in 1902. Henry's daughter, Eleanor, married Joseph W. Wittmann; together they promoted the rebuilding of Walnut Grove Dam and the construction of a dam in Box Canyon—a few miles north of Wickenburg (see page 95)—that would supply water to the Nadaburg area (see Chapter 6, page 93). In 1929 the town of Nadaburg was renamed Wittmann.

Chapter 2:
Hassayampa River

The Hassayampa River originates on the slope of Mt. Union in central Arizona and ends at its confluence with the Gila River (see map in Preface). There are several versions of the origin of the name of the river. Local lore says simply that the name is Indian meaning "River that runs upside down" or "water that is hidden" because most of the time the flow is underground in many sections of the river. That definition appears to be unlikely. Two more likely definitions are:

1. *ha-sa-ya-mo*, a Yavapai word meaning "following the water as far as it goes" (Corbusier, 1969, p. 68). William Henry Corbusier was an army surgeon who was stationed at Fort Date Creek (north of Wickenburg and west of Prescott) and at Camp Verde. He learned some of the Yavapai language and at times was close to the Yavapai people. Three books—one by Dr. Corbusier himself, one by his wife, Fanny, and one by his son, William Tremaine Corbusier—describe his experiences. The book cited above is by the son. The Wickenburg Chamber of Commerce web site says that the Yavapai "named this place [where they grew crops] Haseyamo,

'following the water as far as it goes,' from which the word Hassayampa [is] derived."

2. Lloyd (1933) gives two definitions: (1) *aha-sa-ya-mo* meaning "running water" and (2) *ha-ha-yama-pa* meaning "the river of the place of big rocks." James (1917, p. 362) gives the latter definition and attributes the words to either the Hualapai or Yavapai. Granger (1983, p. 292) attributes the name to the Mohave words *ah* meaning "water," *si-am* meaning "big rocks" and *pa* meaning "place of" and lists alternate spellings as *haviamp*, *aziamp* and *ah-ha-seyampa*.

Actually, both definitions—and more—may be correct as the Yavapai had several divisions, each with a slightly different dialect. The name has been attributed to Pauline Weaver. However, Conner (1956) uses Haviamp in his exploration with the Walker party implying that it is what the Indians called the river. He states that it is a "pure Indian word" pronounced with a strong accent on the last syllable." It is said to take on its modern spelling from a recorder who kept books for the Weaver Mining District and Conner says that "Mr. Wheelhouse, while arranging his records, ... spelled 'Hassayampa', which has been sustained by our geographies ...". Many other books and articles have cited one of the above meanings, probably the first that the author came across. The exact origin seems to be lost to the vagueness of history.

Someone not familiar with the Southwest might not recognize the Hassayampa as a river and, indeed, it has often been called a creek. Although the flow is hidden in the sand in parts of the river, appearing on the surface only in wet periods, even during low water times the water does appear on the surface in places where the river passes over a bedrock ledge or where bedrock is only a short distance under the surface.

The river through Wickenburg—the largest town on the banks of the Hassayampa—usually appears to be dry. Some wag has posted a sign on each end of the highway bridge that says, "No fishing from bridge." Perhaps the tourists don't understand that Wickenburg residents are protective of the sand trout. The next time that you eat at a Wickenburg restaurant, ask for sand trout even if you don't see it on the menu.

After the failure of the dam the following article appeared in the *Washington Post* (March 2, 1890, p. 14):

> **With a Canteen of Water.** The recent calamity by the bursting of the dam at Walnut Grove, on the Hassayampa, in Arizona, recalls a story in regard to that stream. The Hassayampa is almost entirely dry a portion of the year, there being only an occasional hole of stagnant water. Some official of the Fish Commission, with a view of stocking the stream, wrote to inquire what species of fish were desired with which to stock the stream. He was answered that the question was not definitely settled, but that the last fish seen in that vicinity was working itself up the bed of the stream with a canteen around its neck looking for water.

Perhaps the intermittent[1] nature of the river inspired the "legend of the Hassayampa"[2]:

> There is a legend centuries old,
> by the early Spaniards told
> of a sparkling stream that "Lies"
> under Arizona skies.
> Hassayampa is its name
> and the title to its fame
> is a wondrous quality
> known today from sea to sea.
> Those who drink its waters bright
> red man, white man, boor or knight,
> girls or women, boys or men,
> never tell the truth again!
>
> You've heard about the wondrous stream
> They say it turns a thoughtful guy
> into a lying scamp
> and if you quaff its waters once
> you'll ne'er forsake the blasted stream
> or tell the truth again.

The legend has had occasional notice in the eastern press. In 1938 New York City Mayor Fiorello LaGuardia received gifts from an old prospector who had arrived from Arizona

---

1. Two words that are often confused are "intermittent" and "ephemeral." Ephemeral streams flow only after precipitation or snow melt. Intermittent streams flow constantly, but in some stretches the flow may be below the surface except after precipitation. The Hassayampa is intermittent.
2. Written by Andrew Downing. The date is uncertain but appears to be near the end of the nineteenth century.

with three burros. On one of the burros were two barrels of Hassayampa River water. The mayor, having spent his boyhood in Prescott, knew of the legend and declined to drink from the barrels; however, he said that he might give some to members of the City Council (*New York Times*, Apr. 26, 1939, p. 14).

Some regard the legend as giving a negative view of the river. Apparently to counter such an image, John Mitchell wrote an alternate poem[3]:

> "Hassayampa—Queen of Waters,"
> There is magic in the name;
> It's a fascinating stream when all is said,
> And everybody knows who has wandered where it flows
> There's a legend for each pebble in its bed.
> But, best of all, the story of the noble pioneers
> Who hailed it a good omen on their way,
> And those loyal men and true have imbued it through
> With the Arizona spirit of today.
> For the Hassayampa's water is a blessing to the land—
> (In spite of shocking tales with which it's cursed—
> That he ever after lies in a way to win first prize,
> Who quaffs the Hassayamp' to quench his thirst).
> Salvation of the farmer, and the miner's friend in need.
> It makes the man who drinks it brave and true. And no
> matter where he stays he'll come back to end his days
> In the land the Hassayampa wanders through.

---

3. ublished in the *Arizona Republic* in 1896 and written in *Buckaroo*, Volunteer Newsletter of the Desert Caballeros Western Museum, February 2008.

Water Uses

Long before Arizona was invaded by Europeans, the Indians used the Hassayampa for irrigation. A virtual desert oasis exists about three miles south of Wickenburg where the river runs on the surface throughout the year. This area was apparently occupied during the winter months, at least, and used for various crops. After Phoenix became a population center, it was named the Garden of Allah and became a spot for a few people to escape the heat of the Salt River Valley. Today it is part of the Hassayampa River Preserve (see map in Preface), owned and operated by The Nature Conservancy, containing a museum and nature trails.

During the gold rush era, the Hassayampa provided water for crops as well as water used in the mines and for the separation of gold from the ore-bearing rock. The banks of the river through Wickenburg were croplands and the river was lined by arrastras. Both the farms and the arrastras were destroyed by the flood after the failure of the dam and never restored. For a time the river had a pumping station south of Wickenburg (at Seymour) that provided water to the Vulture Mine (see map in Preface).

Today, the entire river remains almost undammed. Hassayampa Lake, only 1.66 acres in area, is two miles from the originating spring. If that tiny lake is discounted, the Hassayampa is one of only three rivers in Arizona (the others being the San Pedro and Santa Cruz, both in the southern part of the state) without a controlling dam. Since Arizona has few natural lakes, any body of water provides a valuable resource for recreation. The short-lived reservoir behind Walnut Grove Dam was used for recreational purposes as shown in Figure 2-1.

Figure 2-1. Recreation on the lake behind Walnut Grove Dam. (Taken by G. I. Gardener circa 1888. Provided courtesy of John Cooper).

The Watershed

The drainage basin of the Hassayampa (1471 square miles) is one of the most mineral-rich areas of the world. Most of the minerals occur in the upper 800 square miles. Although known primarily for its gold, mines have produced commercial quantities of silver, copper, feldspar, lead, vermiculite and even kitty litter. Elevations in the watershed range from 7989 feet above sea level at Mt. Union—the Hassayampa begins at a spring at elevation 7380 feet on the slope of Mt. Union—to 790 feet at its confluence with the Gila River. A notation on the flow record near the Gila River states, "no natural flow for most of time each year," which neglects the underground flow. Peak flows at the Morristown gage (drainage area of 796 square miles) are more than that of the gage near the Gila since the width of the river and the flood plain increase considerably south of Morristown. The total length of the river is 118 miles with the Walnut Grove Dam site 30 miles from the originating spring.

Those who have written or given testimony about the dam have come up with a wide variety of numbers for the drainage area upstream of the Walnut Grove Dam site:

—311 sq. mi. (Schuyler, 1901, p. 63; Charles D. Walcott, Director USGS, 1897, U. S. Congressional Series Set 3646)

—390 sq. mi. (Wagoner, 1888, p. 73)

—320,000 sq. mi. (Powell, 1892, pp. 228–229; a misprint?)

—325 sq. mi. (Dutton, 1890, p. 138).

—500 sq. mi. (*Engineering News*, March, 1890, p. 206).

—150 sq. mi. (Washington Letter, 1890)

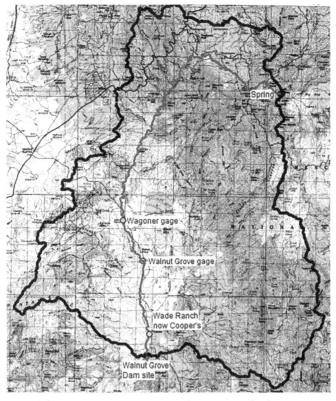

Figure 2-2. The Hassayampa River and its watershed upstream of the Walnut Grove Dam site.

These listings are, no doubt, a result of wild guesses and generally poor maps in the late 19th century. The USGS has specified the water-shed area at the Walnut Grove stream gage—9.8 miles upstream of the dam site and 24.6 miles downstream of the originating spring—as 107 square miles and at the Box Canyon gage—24.1 miles downstream of the dam site—as 417 square miles. An interpolation of the watershed area based on river distance gives 197 square miles (linear) or 177 square miles (quadratic) at the dam site. My own, admittedly crude, measurement from USGS topo maps (Figure 2-2) gives a value of 263 square miles.

With little idea of what the rainfall might be and only rough guesses at the drainage area, flood flow was impossible to calculate in the 19th century.

The upper reaches of the watershed are forested[4] and inside the Prescott National Forest, the largest stand of Ponderosa pine in the world. From the dense stands of pine trees[5], the river proceeds downward through grasslands and semi-desert growth to

---

4. Major John Wesley Powell in his testimony before Congress stated: "The mountains are not clad with forest. A few scattered trees grow, but in the main the mountains are naked, solid rock" (Powell, 1892, pp. 228–229). Perhaps Major Powell had never been to this area. It's puzzling that Brodie, an engineer on the dam, made a similar statement (page 131). Stromberg, et al. (1993, p. 119) got it right: "The watershed area above [Wickenburg] is about [695 square miles], approximately one-third of which is composed of mountains vegetated by *Pinus ponderosa* forests."

5. The forest has changed since the 19th century. There were fewer trees then but many more large trees, giving the area a park-like appearance. The mistaken policy of fire suppression has allowed the smaller trees to grow and choke the forest. These, plus an accumulation of forest litter, provide fuel and a "ladder" for smaller fires to become very large so that they can kill the large trees.

the site of the Walnut Grove Dam. From there it flows through rugged desert topography and a canyon to Wickenburg and Morristown. Downstream from Morristown the terrain is relatively flat, low desert (see map in Preface). The winter snowpack is often several feet in the upper reaches but varies greatly from year to year. At the lower end of the river, mean annual rainfall is about 7.9 inches and snow is all but unknown—a remarkable change of climate for a river only 118 miles long (78 miles straight line from the originating spring to the Gila River).

Dam-Site Flow Calculations

A crucial part of the design of a dam is the determination of the river flows. On one hand the flow must be sufficient for the intended use, and in the case of the Walnut Grove Dam, W. H. Bates had a difficult time convincing eastern investors that Arizona had sufficient rainfall to fill the reservoir, one of many ironies considering the ultimate result of the project. (Perhaps the belief in the aridity of the region was the reason that a larger spillway was not constructed.) On the other hand, the project must be designed so that it can withstand the largest flows. A culvert across a minor highway might be designed to withstand a flood that recurs in a period as short as five or ten years. A major dam project, where failure means large financial losses and loss of life, must be designed to withstand a *very* rare event, perhaps the 1000-year flood or even the "maximum probable" flood. The Walnut Grove Dam—although small compared to other, more recent, dams in the state such as Roosevelt, Hoover and Glen Canyon—falls in the latter category; it should have been designed to withstand the maximum flood that the Hassayampa could produce.

An examination of the records of the Walnut Grove Dam indicates very little in the way of calculation of the relevant quantity of flow that could be expected. I could find nothing that would give the investors' confidence that there was sufficient water for the intended hydraulic mining. Obviously, extensive rainfall and flow data were not available in the late 19th century and the engineers who designed the dam were probably not familiar with Arizona rivers. Luther Wagoner, one of the engineers, used high water marks to estimate flood flows. He states (*Engineering News*, April 5, 1890, p. 328):

> An examination of high marks near and below the dam showed that ordinary flood discharge was about 10,000 cu. ft. per second, and evidence existed that at no remote period the discharge was perhaps as great as 25,000 cu. ft. per second.

That statement was made after the dam failure and at a time when Wagoner was attempting to deflect blame away from himself. Nevertheless, these numbers are not bad guesses (see Appendix II).

Unfortunately, the streamflow record is so spotty that there is no good data at the dam site even today. Pope, et al. (1998) show five USGS stream gages on the Hassayampa at various times and locations[6]. The Flood Control District of Maricopa County has data for four gages; they also have calculated the 2-, 5-, 10-, 25-, 50and 100-year flood flows. The existing record is shown in Table 1.

---

6. For peak flows in Arizona from the USGS see http://nwis.waterdata.usgs. gov/ az/nwis/peak. If you sort by county, Wagoner, Walnut Grove and Box Canyon are in Yavapai County; Morristown and Arlington are in Maricopa County. The FCDMC web site is http://www.fcd.maricopa.gov/index.aspx

Table 1. Stream gages on the Hassayampa River

Gage location	Dist from dam[a] (miles)	Drainage area (miles^2)	Max recorded flow (cfs)	Years of record	100-year flow (cfs)
Wagoner (USGS)	-9.9	78.70	1700	7	-----
Wagoner (FCDMC)	-9.9	78	5068	14.85	17,100
Walnut Grove (USGS)	-6.8	107	294	2	-----
Box Canyon (USGS)	24	417	58,000[b]	41	-----
Box Canyon (FCDMC)	24	417	19,094	14.96	67,700
Wickenburg (FCDMC)	32.0	711	16,089	12.55	50,500
Morristown (USGS)	39.5	796	47,500	61	-----
Morristown (FCDMC)	39.5	796	14,962	9.4	37,000
Arlington (USGS)	80.8	1471	39,000	44	-----

a. To complete the distance column, the originating spring is -34.3 miles, and the Gila River is 83.3 miles, making the total Hassayampa length 117.6 miles.
b. See page 88.

None of these gages is at the dam site. Both the Walnut Grove gage and the Wagoner gage are upstream of the dam site (see map, Figure 2-2) and their records are too short to be of much use. The Wagoner gage might have been correlated with the

Box Canyon gage, but the seven years of record do not include any high flows, and the two highest years are missing from the Box Canyon gage. It seems that no meaningful correlation for high flows between gages is possible. Those who call economics the "dismal science" have not studied hydrology.

At the Box Canyon gage the maximum flow of record (USGS) is 58,000 cfs (Pope, et al., 1998) recorded September 5, 1970. That quantity has a footnote that says it is the highest flow since 1890. The authors could not have known the maximum flow in 1890, but stream gagers will frequently look for high water marks and/or talk to knowledgeable people about past floods. In that way they probably found evidence of at least one flow greater than 58,000 cfs and attributed it to the dam beak of 1890.

My own guess for the floods at the dam site for various return periods is given in Table 2 based on the Wagoner calculation and the ratio of drainage areas.

Table 2. Estimated flood flows (cfs) at the Walnut Grove Dam site for various return periods.

	2-year	5-year	10-year	20-year	50-year	100-year
Flow	1608	6474	12,812	22,017	39,450	57,658

All who have written about the dam failure have said that the flood flow was exceptional, something that could not have been predicted. For example, Brodie in his report to Van Beuren (Appendix III) stated: "The flood, which resulted so disastrously for the Company and caused the breaking of the storage dam, on the morning of the 22d of February last, was one of unprecedented ferocity..." and "... within the memory of man there never had been so general and heavy a rain resulting in such terrible floods." But if the calculations (Appendix II) above are anywhere near correct, the less that 23,000 cfs passing down the river was about the 20-year flood, certainly not unprecedented. The dam should have been designed to withstand a flow of, perhaps, five times that amount.

CHAPTER 3:
DAMS AND "HYDRAULICKING"

Hydraulic mining was used as early as 1852 (Bowie, 1885)[1] or 1853 (http://en.wikipedia.org/wiki/Hydraulic_mining) in California to wash gold bearing sands and gravels into an open flume that had a corrugated bottom or was otherwise configured to trap the heavier particles. Hydraulic mining, dredging, and panning are forms of placer mining, the separation of gold from alluvial deposits that are the results of erosion of gold-bearing rocks. Prior to the construction of the Walnut Grove Dam, hydraulic mining was used in California, Nevada, Colorado, South Dakota, Idaho, and Montana. The Walnut Grove project was late in coming to this game. In Arizona hydraulic mining was carried out in Lynx Creek[2]—south of Prescott close to the Hassayampa River but not in the Hassayampa watershed—in the 1890s. Since the purpose of the Walnut Grove Dam was hydraulic mining, this chapter is included to illustrate what might have been. The best examples are from California.

---

1. Bowie has a history of hydraulic mining internationally; it is especially detailed in the California aspects.

2. Sharlot Hall Museum in Prescott has a photograph of the Lynx Creek operation. Considerable dredging took place on Lynx Creek in later years. Robinson (1919, p. 257) reports that over a million dollars worth of gold was taken from the placer deposits. The area, including Lynx Lake, is now a place for recreation.

The Process

The classic picture (Figure 3-1) of the prospector and his donkey was a true representation of early gold mining in the West. The prospector sought both placer deposits and hard-rock veins. Indeed, if gold appeared in the sands of a streambed, it must have originated somewhere higher in the watershed where, perhaps, it could be mined at its source. However, the alluvial deposits were relatively easy to work and sometimes yielded large quantities of gold, but using the prospector's pan was slow and inefficient.

Figure 3-1. Gold panning continues today, but it is not a way to get rich (courtesy of the Denver Public Library Western History collection).

A much grander method employed a dredge that utilized a steam engine. It could scoop up large quantities of sand and gravel to be placed in a sluice that separated the gold. Dredges could often be floated up rivers to the alluvial deposits. They were also dismantled, carried to the streams and reassembled where they could be either floated or placed on tracks. But in many locations the streams were too small and/or too remote to use dredges.

If a source of water could be found, there was another method to get the material into the sluices—hydraulic mining, some-times termed "hydraulicking." The process consisted of direct-ing jets of water into the stream bed and the surrounding banks to wash sand, gravel and even rocks into a flume that could trap the heavier particles. The catch, of course, was securing a reliable water source since the stream alone often did not have sufficient flow throughout the typical year. In many places, and especially in the Southwest, many streams and rivers have lit-tle or no flow most of the time but can occasionally have enor-mous floods. Dams could store the flood flows and raise the head (pressure) of the water to provide a reliable source and the velocity necessary to dig out the alluvium and wash it into the separating *sluice.*

Figure 3-2 shows jets of water directed against an alluvial deposit in Mineral County, Colorado. Given enough velocity, the water could bring down not only the loose deposits in and near the stream bed but also the more or less hard rock of can-yon walls. It might not wash the material directly into a sluice but first put it through a crusher to create small particles.

Figure 3-2. Hydraulic mining in Mineral County, Colorado (courtesy of the Denver Public Library Western History collection)

The destruction caused by the water jet could be enormous. In the case of the so-called "Little Giant" and the "Monitor" machines, the size of the nozzle was from four to nine inches in diameter, discharging from 13 to 25 cubic feet per second of water under a head of from three to five hundred feet. An eight-inch nozzle used by the North Bloomfield Gravel Mining Company on the Yuba River in California discharged 51 cubic feet per second at a velocity of 150 feet per second[3].

The Dams

An account of early dams in the West is available in Schuyler's books (1901 and 1909) and in Bowie's book (1885). In general,

---

3. From court records in the case of *Woodruff v. North Bloomfield Gravel Mining Company*, Jan. 7, 1884.

dams may be of the gravity type, where the mass of the dam is sufficient to hold back the water, or the structural type, where the dam is built of material sufficiently strong to withstand the force of the water on the upstream face. The former includes earth dams, massive concrete dams and rockfill dams; the latter comprises arch dams—usually made of concrete—steel dams, and wooden dams. The type of dam depends on local conditions and the availability of materials. Concrete arch dams (e.g., Hoover and Glen Canyon in Arizona) are constructed in hard-rock canyons with steep walls that can withstand the stress that is transmitted from the dam to the canyon walls. Earth dams are nearly the opposite. They are constructed where the river valley does not have steep sides and they are usually longer and not as high as the arch dams. The force of the water is more likely to be transmitted to the stream bed than canyon walls. Sometimes a dam is a combination of types, e.g., a rockfill dam with a steel core and/or a concrete foundation.

The gold areas of the West in the 19th century were often remote from roads and in rugged locations. Moreover, the arch dam had not been used at that time or was not sufficiently analyzed to assure its safety. The streams often had the requisite geometry for structural dams and concrete gravity dams, but the cost of transporting concrete to the site could be prohibitive. In addition, the purpose for the stored water—hydraulic mining—had a lifetime of only a decade or two before the commercial quantities of gold played out, making the economic life of the dams temporary, in contrast to water supply for irrigation and domestic use that goes on into the indefinite future. Thus, dams needed to be constructed of local material at minimum cost and did not need to last for very long periods. The Walnut Grove Dam fit the criteria for a rockfill dam, which was selected as the type that was built.

The rockfill dam is basically a pile of rock—rubble—placed across a stream. There are a number of basic varieties. The earliest was the crib type where the rock, usually small stone, was placed in a wooden and/ or wire box and these boxes were stacked to form the dam. They were generally, but not always, considered temporary since the wood would rot leaving loose stone that could be washed away.

Other types of rockfill dams used larger rock—usually under 150 lbs so that they could be handled, but sometimes huge boulders were used. The rock was dumped in the river to form a barrier that was sufficiently massive to withstand the force of the ponded water without sliding or tipping. Leakage was always a problem as water could easily pass through the rock matrix. Waterproofing was accomplished by one or a combination of the following: (a) using a central steel or concrete wall in the dam, (b) placing concrete on the upstream face of the dam, (c) placing a barrier of wood, tar paper and caulking on the upstream face (the method used at Walnut Grove), (d) using a clay barrier in the dam and/or (e) using hydraulically ponded clay interior to the dam or against the upstream face. For more on leaks see page 68.

The rate of failure of early dams seems to have been quite high. Some of the failures were catastrophic, as was the case at Walnut Grove. Others simply passed the water downstream, perhaps temporarily flooding farmland but doing little damage. As the population density of this country has increased in the last hundred years, dam safety has become a major source of controversy and has led to the organization of the Association of State Dam Safety Officials (ASDSO) and the push for federal and state laws (see the section on dam safety, page 44) to increase oversight of dam construction and to inspect existing dams. Nevertheless, ASDSO has identified a huge number of dams in the U.S. that are dangerous with their potential failure leading to loss of life and property.

Environmental Concerns

Nineteenth century miners did not give a thought to the environment in their rush for riches, although the individual prospector with his gold pan did little to harm the environment. Damage was a different matter for more sophisticated methods whether the mines were underground or on the surface. Gold extraction using acid or mercury has the potential to contaminate surface streams and underground aquifers. Mine tailings often contain heavy metals that are harmful to animals and humans and can leach out into the surrounding environment[4].

Thousands of abandoned underground mines remain holes in the ground that are dangerous traps for the unwary. Mines with horizontal shafts lure the foolish to explore them, not realizing that they have not been scaled for decades so that the danger of falling rock—or even a cave-in—is considerable, and they may contain snakes, lizards, spiders, bats, bees, scorpions and other creatures. A current controversy in Arizona is how to pay for cleaning and closing of old sites. *The Arizona Republic* (July 26, 2008, p. 1) reports that "at least 12 people died in abandoned-mine accidents from 2004 to 2007 [in Arizona, California and Nevada]."

---

4. The United States is still (in 2009) operating under the Mining Law of 1872, which many have severely criticized as hopelessly outdated. The primary points of controversy are economic—no royalty payment to the government for extraction of minerals on public land—and insufficient environmental protection.

Nothing, however, has damaged the environment as much as surface mining of rivers and streams. A dredge pretty much destroys everything in its path, creating an awful mess as the gold-bearing sands are separated from their riches and returned to the stream as piles of loose sediment to be washed downstream in the next flood. At least the dredge only digs into the stream bed, somewhat limiting its effect.

Hydraulic mining has all the disadvantages of the dredge and more. It devastates the stream, kills all the fish and other creatures that depend on the water and creates piles of sediment not only from the stream bed but also from the alluvial material (and perhaps rock) of the sides. Nothing escapes, not only in the vicinity of the mine but far downstream, perhaps to the end of the river or creek. This sediment is placed in a stream that nature did not design to carry it. The sediment will deposit out at some point, often ruining farms and creating flooding. It is a man-made mess that can last for a century or more. I quote extensively from the case of *Woodruff v. North Bloomfield Gravel Mining Company*[5] in the California Circuit Court.

Numerous examples of damage are cited in the court proceedings; some of them are:

> At its escape from the mountains, where the foot-hills recede and give width to the plain, the Yuba [River] spreads out its load of sand and gravel over a plain of fifteen thousand to sixteen thousand acres, which has risen until it now stands above the level of the adjoining country on either side. This plain has a slope of

---

5 Bowie (1885) discusses the operations of the North Bloomfield Gravel Mining Company in some detail.

about ten feet to the mile, varying above and below this limit as you ascend or descend, the slope of the river bed being fifteen feet at the foot-hills and five feet at Marysville [California], ten miles below. The sizes of material have some correspondence to the grades. Ascending the stream, one passes to a continually increasing average size of material. While it is nearly all sand below, above it becomes nearly all gravel, with, however, considerable admixture of different sizes everywhere. This irruption from the mountains has destroyed thousands of acres of alluvial land. The [California] state engineer, in 1880, estimated that fifteen thousand two hundred and twenty acres had been seriously injured by these deposits from the Yuba.

Dr. Teegarden's lands afford a very striking example of individual injuries inflicted by this mining debris. Dr. Teegarden is a prominent citizen of Yuba county, having for some years represented that county in the state senate. He owned 1,275 acres on the Yuba bottoms, some three or four miles above Marysville, on the north side. All except the 75 acres now lying outside the levee have been buried from three to five feet deep with sand, and utterly destroyed for farming purposes; for which injuries he has received no remuneration.

Levees had to be built to contain the flooding caused by filling the Yuba River channel with sediment, but:

Not only has all the space between these levees been filled with this debris to a level with the highlands upon which they are built, but for miles of the lower portion of the river the filling between the levees is several feet above the level of the surrounding country on the outside.

The intervening space is grown up with young cottonwoods and willows. The river has now no definite channel within these bounds, but runs anywhere over the space between the levees, situate two to three miles apart, according to the obstructions its waters meet from time to time by growing trees, or accumulations of drift-wood, or deposits made by itself, thereby raising the bed, where it actually for a time runs, to a higher level than the bed of such surrounding channel as it has. This broad channel or bed, such as it is, is several feet higher than the lands of the surrounding country outside the levees, which outside lands have no protection from overflow of the waters of the Yuba, surcharged with debris, except the slender intervening artificial banks so erected by the people and the miners for that purpose. The lands thus already buried and destroyed are over 15,000 acres, or 25 square miles; or, taking the average width, a tract from the foot-hills to Marysville, twelve miles long along the river by two miles wide. The filling in the river bed is generally 25 feet or more, and, at its immediate junction with Feather river at Marysville, is about 20 feet deep,-some witnesses make it deeper,-where it forms a bar of nearly that depth across Feather river. The depth of the filling is increasing year by year and raising the bed of the river within the levees higher and higher above the surrounding country outside the levees. The depth of the filling increases as the river is ascended, till at Squaw flat, near Park's bar, below Smartsville, at the entrance of the foot-hills, according to the testimony of O'Brien, a witness for defendants, it is 150 feet deep. Opposite Sucker-Flat ravine it is 90, and at the narrows above Smartsville, 60 feet deep. The deposits constituting the first 50 feet, at Squaw flat, have been there 10 or 12 years, and the rest has accumulated since. At a point near this, at Rose's bar, where the channel was once but 100 to 300 feet wide in the bed of the canyon, it has now been raised by filling till it is 3,000 feet wide.

Is it hardly beneficial to have a river run through a community when:

> The waters of the Yuba are so charged with debris that they are wholly unfit for watering stock, or for any of the uses, domestic or otherwise, to which water is usually applied, without being first taken out of the stream and allowed to stand in some undisturbed place and settle. As it comes down to Marysville it is so heavily charged with sand as to render it unfit even for surface irrigation.

These problems continue to where the Yuba River empties into the Feather River and the Feather into the Sacramento River.

If there was any one item of good that resulted from the failure of Walnut Grove Dam, it was that hydraulic mining did not take place in the Hassayampa River watershed.

Legal

Given the environmental destruction, the consequences of which are not borne by the miners but primarily by those using the stream and living near it downstream from the mining, what are the legal ramifications of hydraulic mining? The construction of Walnut Grove Dam began in 1886, but an 1884 landmark decision in the California Circuit Court put the downstream costs squarely on the mining companies and greatly altered the economics of hydraulic mining. Judge Sawyer in the case of *Woodruff v. North Bloomfield Gravel Mining Company*, which was sued by a group of farmers, stated in his decision:

> The acts of hydraulic mining companies in permitting the tailings and debris from their mines to flow into navigable rivers, so as to fill up and obstruct the navigation thereof, and to flood the lands of private persons, and so cover them with sediment as to destroy their value for agricultural purposes, constitute both a public and a private nuisance, unless authorized by positive provision of law; and the owners may bring suit in equity to restrain the further commission of such nuisance.

> The deposit of tailings and debris from hydraulic mines in navigable streams, so as to obstruct navigation and flood and depreciate private lands, is not authorized or permitted by the statutes of the United States regulating mining on the public lands, or by the California statutes relating to mining or to the improvement of navigable rivers, or by the customs of miners. ... The fact that a statute recognizes the legality of a certain occupation, and makes provision for its regulation, to prevent injury from its conduct, does not justify or legalize such business, so as to prevent its abatement, where it becomes a public nuisance.

In 1886 the North Bloomfield Gravel Mining Company was again brought to court and found in contempt for violating the 1884 order to stop putting debris in the river. The Company's luck in court was not all bad. In 1891 Woodruff brought another contempt case against the Company, this time losing when the Company was found not guilty. In 1892 the United States sought a court order to enjoin the Company from continuing its hydraulic mining operations so as to obstruct or endanger the navigation of certain rivers. The injunction was denied. In 1897 the Company sued the United States alleging that the surrendering to the United States the right to regulate the disposal of the debris violated the Constitution by taking property rights without compensation. North Bloomfield lost that one.

These cases against the North Bloomfield Gravel Mining Company were not the only ones involving that company and they certainly were not the first or last involving mining operations that put sediment into rivers and streams. In 1893 the California Debris Commission was formed to insure that hydraulic mining could not be continued without a permit and to take steps to restore navigability of a river to its former condition of 1851 or 1852, about the time California was ceded to the Union. It consisted of three members, employees of the U.S. Army Corps of Engineers, appointed by the President of the United States. Mining companies took the position that possession of a permit and approval by the Debris Commission absolved them from liability, but the courts held otherwise and made them responsible for damage caused by hydraulic mining. As far as I know, no cases involving hydraulic mining have been brought in Arizona.

However, one has to wonder if liability considerations were taken into account by the investors of the Walnut Grove Water

Storage Company. In fact, many of these considerations continue more than a century later. In 2003 in the case of *Peter Paterno v. State of California et al.* concerning damage caused by a failed levee, Judge Morrison made the comment:

> The environmental aftermath of the Gold Rush continues to plague California.

CHAPTER 4: COLLAPSE

As Assistant Superintendent Brown[1] watched three-foot deep-water pass over the dam, he probably did not calculate its velocity, about 5.35 ft/sec. At the bottom of the dam it had reached a speed near 80 ft/ sec (55 mph) with an average depth of about 10 inches. Averages at this point are meaningless, however, as the flow was two-dimensional due to the converging sides and was a frothy, wavy torrent. Brown didn't need to do the calculations to be certain that the dam was doomed. In fact, he had sent two riders downstream the previous afternoon to warn those below that a flood was coming[2].

According to brothers Moses and Robert Moore, the water had reached the bottom of the spillway about 4 o'clock (*San Francisco Chronicle*, Feb. 27, 1890, p. 6). Captain Hunt, who was on watch with Superintendent Brown when the dam gave way

---

1. The printed accounts name Brown as superintendent, but Brodie had the title of "Engineer and Superintendent." Brown served under Brodie. In court testimony he was called "Sub-superintendent."

2. Dr. Mabel Amanda Genung was the first woman physician in Arizona and the daughter of Charles B. and Ida Genung, early pioneers. She recounts much of the early history of the region in letters to Eleanor B. Sloan, former director of the Arizona Historical Society. In one of the letters Dr. Genung stated that the riders were sent by "Postmaster Wagoner at lower Walnut Grove." The story is continued as told in all printed accounts and the letter by Brodie (Appendix III) that Brown was responsible for sending the messengers.

said the first sign of the break was the snapping of a large steel cable connecting the tower in the middle of the dam with the bank. The next instant the tower tottered and it seemed as if the entire dam moved bodily at once. The roar of the waters and the grinding of the boulders were deafening.

The flood

Eyewitness accounts indicate that the collapse occurred almost instantaneously. Flow through the river where the dam had stood increased to the tremendously large *instantaneous* value of 846,900 cfs, undoubtedly more than anything that the river had experienced[3]. The flood wave proceeded down the Hassayampa River Canyon attenuating only modestly as it proceeded (Figure 4-1)[4]. The flood reached the site of the Lower dam in 40 minutes and crested at 65 feet an hour after failure, sweeping away everything and causing the greatest loss of life of any location. The depth was about the same in Box Canyon, where the narrow section of the river formed an obstruction, cresting in an hour and 40 minutes. Downstream from Box Canyon the maximum depth dropped considerably as evidenced at Rincon Road where it was only 37 feet. Further attenuation brought the maximum depth to only 15 feet in the vicinity of the present-day US 60 bridge. The depth grew again to 28 feet where the river is confined to a narrower valley near the Hassayampa River Preserve (Brill's farm). The fields at Brill's farm were covered in sand but the buildings (approximately 25 feet above the

---

3. On the other hand, extreme flows do occur naturally. One that has received considerable study occurred in Plum Creek near Denver in 1965 (Osterkamp and Costa, 1987). It was 15 times the 50-year flood.

4. See Appendix II, page 124, for an explanation of the flood calculation.

river level) were not washed away. From the printed accounts I judge that the computed depth in that location may be slightly too high, but, in general, they confirm my calculation.

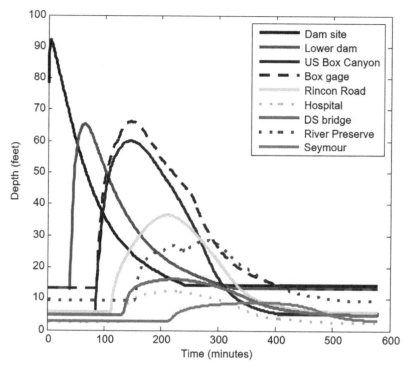

Figure 4-1. Depth in the river vs time after failure for various locations as calculated by the program HEC-RAS (see page 124). Rincon Road, Hospital and DS (downstream of the present-day) bridge represent the Wickenburg depths, the latter at Henry Wickenburg's farm. The River Preserve is at Brill's farm. The depth at the dam is a bit higher than that calculated in Appendix II (see Damsite flow at failure, page 126) due to a different algorithm. The flow hydrograph appears as Figure II-1.

Further downstream the river enters into a wide floodplain. At Seymour the maximum depth was only 8.5 feet, enough to cause a substantial loss of property and a drowning at Smith's mill, a short distance downstream from Seymour.

Seven hours after collapse the river was still in a serious state of flooding through Wickenburg, but the effects of the dam collapse had largely disappeared.

People[5]

William Akard and Dan Burke

The first of the riders, setting out at 3:00 p.m. on February 21 (*San Francisco Chronicle*, Feb. 27, 1890, p. 6), was Dan Burke, a prospector working as a blacksmith making $6 per day. By all accounts Dan stopped at the nearest saloon[6] and got stinking drunk, thus failing to warn people downstream. Some publications report that no one believed Dan when he told them that the dam was about to break and he became discouraged; however, that was not apparent in the newspapers at the time and Burke's statement in his own defense (*Prescott Morning Courier*, Mar. 13, 1890) did not mention that he wasn't believed. Perhaps Brown anticipated that Burke would prove unreliable—Dill (1987, p. 298) characterized him as a "habitual drunkard"—or perhaps he decided that Burke needed a backup, but he sent a second rider at 8:30 p. m. (*San Francisco Chronicle*, Feb. 27, 1890, p. 6) named William Akard and by some accounts—e.g., the *Phoenix Daily Herald* (Feb. 27)—a third rider, James Cameron. I

5. The accounts of this section depend primarily on newspaper stories in spite of my skepticism about such articles. The first—the story of William Akard—illustrates that newspapers get it wrong.

6. The saloon was Goodwin Station; its location is uncertain. Various articles have specified different locations. The most credible is that by Willson (1965) that says it must have been somewhere on Oak Creek (3.5 river miles downstream of the dam) or Cherry Creek (0.8 miles). An article in the *Wickenburg Sun* (Oct. 2, 1961; reprinted July 21, 1969) identifies the saloon as "Boulder Pat's Saloon ... located halfway between the two dams ..." That article is so full of errors that I give it little credence.

think that the name Cameron has become confused with the ranch owner *so* that Burke and Akard were the only messengers[7]. Dill (1987, *p.* 298) reported that "Akard lost his life in the river within sight of the diversion *[Lower]* dam," which *he* probably got *from* the February 26 *Prescott Journal-Miner* or the February 26 *San Francisco Chronicle*: "William Akard could not keep ahead of the flood, and lost his life in trying to cross the Hassayampa within view of the survivors of the camp he had tried to save."

Burke was blamed for much of the loss of life. The *Phoenix Daily Herald* (Mar. 6) wrote, "Dan Burke, who got drunk and thus drowned the Hassayampa victims, was jailed at Prescott last Friday to avoid lynching." He was charged with manslaughter but released. According to the *Arizona Daily Gazette* (Mar. 15): "The people here [Prescott] are indignant over discharge of Dan Burke ... there is no provision of law in Arizona under which he can be punished."

Burke wrote a long letter to the *Prescott Courier* (Mar. 13) in which he denied blame. He enlisted James Cameron as a witness that he was not drunk and was unavoidably delayed, partly because he did not know the trail, although Brown stated that he had chosen Burke because he was very familiar with the territory. In the March 13 issue Cameron had a letter stating that Burke's statements regarding him are "completely false" and that he (Cameron) had found Burke drunk and tried to take his horse to complete the mission but Burke refused.

Frank Goodwin stated that Burke had stopped at his place (Goodwin Station) for about 10 minutes, took a drink of whiskey

---

7. A *Wickenburg Sun* article (see previous footnote) says that Akard and Cameron rode together.

and bought a beer bottle full of whiskey. He then left by the same road on which he had arrived. An hour and a half later he came back saying that he met friends at Cameron's ranch who dared him to come back and get another bottle on credit (*Weekly Journal-Miner*, Mar. 19).

Akard—yes, the same Akard that was supposedly killed near the Lower dam—said in another letter to the *Courier* that he had seen Burke at Cameron's and he was so drunk that he could barely stand. This contradiction seems to be rectified by the *Prescott Morning Courier* of Feb. 24: "The Akard boy went below[8] and it was feared he was overtaken by the water and drowned, but he afterwards returned to the Grove." Akard became a rancher in Peeples Valley, then sold his ranch to the Hays Cattle Company in 1912, the year that the Company was formed. The Hays Ranch is still functioning and owned by John Hays. Akard moved to California where he raised oranges instead of cattle. He died in Whittier, California, in 1955 at age 89. His son, Henry, born in 1916 or 1917, is still living as of 2009.

William O. ("Buckey") O'Neill[9]

Buckey O'Neill was one of the most colorful characters in Territorial Arizona. He arrived in Prescott in 1881 at age

---

8. There is even some doubt that Akard was a courier sent by Brown. The Prescott *Daily Courier* (Oct. 26, 2007) said of Akard and another man: "They turned their horses loose and rode downstream in another man's boat to try to help [after the dam break]." I doubt that any boat could successfully negotiate the river before, during or after the collapse of the dam.

9. The name is spelled "Bucky" in some publications and on the statue honoring the Arizona Rough Riders in the courthouse plaza in Prescott, but "Buckey" is correct. He is said to have acquired this nickname by his love of faro, where he "bucked the tiger."

21 and remained a citizen of that city until his death in the Spanish-American war at San Juan, Cuba, on July 1, 1898. During his career in Arizona he was a court reporter, probate judge, school superintendent, tax collector, miner, captain of the Prescott Grays militia, adjutant general of the Arizona militia, volunteer fireman, sheriff of Yavapai County, mayor of Prescott, editor of the newspaper *Arizona Miner* and publisher of the newspaper *Hoof and Horn*. He ran twice for territorial delegate to Congress as a Populist but lost both times to major party candidates. Buckey must have been an easterner's stereotypical westerner: hard drinking, gambling, and cursing but with an unexpected sophistication. The only thing that he lacked was the square-jawed, tough look (see Figure 4-2).

Figure 4-2. O'Neill as adjutant general of the Arizona Territory, circa 1871.

Buckey assisted Brodie in organizing the Arizona Rough Riders for action in Cuba against Spain in 1898. He commanded Troop A under Brodie, who was the commander of the Arizona Rough Riders and who reported to Lt. Col. Theodore Roosevelt. He is reported to have said: "The Spanish bullet is not molded that will kill me" just before being shot in mouth and killed. That account is disputed by historian Charles Herner and war veterans that he interviewed. Although O'Neill may or may not have made such a statement at some time, he probably did not do so in the moments before his death[10]. He was the first volunteer buried at Arlington National Cemetery. A made-for-television movie by TNT titled "Rough Riders" glamorizes O'Neill (calling him "Bucky") at the expense of historical accuracy.

The Rough Riders are honored in Prescott by a statue on the courthouse square where a man astride a horse that stands on top of a huge block of granite is commonly believed to be O'Neill. Its sculptor, Solon Hannibal Borglum, probably intended the rider to be a nondescript representation of a Rough Rider, but a plaque on the granite block states, "Our 'Bucky [sic] O'Neill' monumental bronze is among [Borglum's] greatest works." A second plaque reads, "Erected by Arizona in honor of the 1st U. S. Volunteer Calvary known to history as Roosevelt's Rough Riders and in memory of Captain William O. O'Neill and his comrades who died while serving their country in the war with Spain."

---

10. Keithley (1949, p. 239) quotes that statement as though O'Neill said it just before the fatal shot. Keithley did not cite sources in his book. Walker (1975, p. 173) says that he spoke those words more than once but does not report that he made the statement immediately before his death.

His fame as sheriff came when he and a small posse tracked train robbers into Utah and captured them after a gun battle. Perhaps his finest moment as sheriff was just after the Walnut Grove Dam failure. Upon receiving word of the collapse, O'Neill left for the dam site with a doctor and several deputies. He reported a scene of multiple horrors: mutilated bodies scattered along the river, survivors suffering in the wet, cold weather clad only in night clothes or grain sacks, and destruction throughout the course of the river. He is said to have been everywhere, working constantly to rescue those who survived and to construct coffins for burial of the dead. He traveled down river to Seymour, well into Maricopa County, where he met Maricopa County Sheriff William Gray. Together they proceeded further down river, still finding bodies.

Mary Hanlon

Mary Hanlon was Van Beuren's niece and living at the camp at the Lower dam at the time of the collapse of the Walnut Grove Dam. According to the February 26 *Prescott Journal-Miner*: "Miss McCarty [Hanlon's maid], a very estimable lady, and Alex. McMillan [Van Beuren's coachman] ... were drowned." Miss Hanlon barely escaped. "She rushed from the house in her night clothes, after vainly but heroically endeavoring to save Miss McCarty, nearly sacrificing her own life in the attempt." She and Mr Reddinton [a hydraulic engineer] "saved themselves by climbing a very steep hill where they remained for several hours."

Hanlon was widely praised for her efforts to administer to the victims of the flood. In a testimonial (*Prescott Morning Courier*, Mar. 20), Chief Justice Wright stated, "... Miss Hanlon performed actions so beautiful that it came to the hearts of this people with a warmth of recognition and admiration, which they cannot describe but will never forget. She is esteemed today and with them her memory will linger, not only as a heroine but as a 'Ministering Angel.'" Hanlon was then presented with a 5.5-ounce gold nugget.

Mary Hanlon later married Brodie and became first lady of the Arizona Territory when he was appointed governor in 1902.

Accounts

The news of the dam failure first appeared in the *New York Times* (Feb. 23, p. 3), the *San Francisco Chronicle* (Feb. 23, p. 15) and the *Washington Post* (Feb. 23, p. 1), all datelined Prescott. Obviously, the amount of news from Arizona was small; the papers devoted about three column-inches to it. The eastern papers had identical wording mentioning Wickenburg where "... great fears are entertained for the safety of that town, but as there is no telegraphic communication no news will be obtainable of its fate until tomorrow at least."

The February 24 articles (page 1) in the *New York Times* held out some hope that the dam had not, in fact, collapsed:

> Yesterday's courier came from the lower dam, and, as the road does not come by the upper dam, it was only surmised that it had given way on account of the immense quantity of water. A more hopeful feeling exists this evening on account of no news being received direct [sic] that the upper dam has given way. It is now hoped that the reservoir is still intact, and that the flood was caused by opening one of the gates to relieve it from the threatening danger.

However, that paragraph conflicts with the remainder of the article, which reports witnesses to the breach in the dam.

On February 26 the *New York Times* (p. 2)—also February 26 in the *Prescott Journal-Miner*—reported that over 50 had drowned and gave a partial list of the names of the dead. That list ended with the notation "and eight Chinamen," which later writers took as a callous disregard for Chinese and blatant racism. The *Phoenix Daily Herald* (Feb. 26) had a list of 13 killed at the lower dam "and two Chinamen." The *Arizona Daily Gazette* (Feb. 27) also published a list of the dead and appended "Seven Mexicans, eight Chinamen." Indeed, racism was alive and well in the Southwest with the pecking order (1) anglos, (2) Mexicans and (3) Chinese[11], but I am inclined to give the newspapers the benefit of doubt in that they simply reported all the information that they had; however, unidentified whites did appear individually in lists as "Unknown." A list in the February 25 *Phoenix Daily Herald* of those known saved at the lower dam included only whites. From the *Prescott Journal-Miner* (Feb. 26): "There were nine Chinamen in camp, eight of whom were lost."

The most extensive coverage of the major newspapers was in the *San Francisco Chronicle*, which ran long articles on February 24, 25, 26, 27, and 28, perhaps because engineers Robinson (page 51) and Wagoner (page 54) were residents of that city. These included long interviews with Wagoner and the paper published a letter from him; Robinson was in Europe at the time. The subject seems to have disappeared from the paper after February 28.

---

11. The Chinese had been brought to North America as laborers to work on the railroads and were used extensively in the California gold rush. How many were used in the construction of the two dams is unknown. A Chinese laundry and a Chinese cafe were located at the Lower dam.

Miscellaneous stories

The following are from newspaper articles. Some of the stories are included here to give a flavor to the aftermath of the dam collapse.

- The town of Seymour was demolished. Mrs. ("Old Mother") Conger was found naked and hungry but alive (*Phoenix Daily Herald*, Feb. 27). Dr. Mabel Genung (see footnote page 31) added to this account[12].

Her mother, Ida Genung, and a hired man, Mike Boland, were traveling to Phoenix "and it was raining. They expected or intended to stay at Seymour. When they arrived at Seymour my mother said, 'Mike hitch up, and we will go on—it's raining and we are between two rivers.' She had baked biscuits and had them in a flour sack. She tied the sack and tossed it to Susie Conger saying, 'You keep this, you might need them.'" When Susie and her partner, Harry Cowell, "heard [the river] roaring [they] grabbed their biscuits and ran up the hill. That was all they had to eat for 3 days."

Mrs. Conger lost "... $1500 in gold coin that was hidden in the roof of her shack" (Mohoney, 1957). She asked the court for a judgment against the Walnut Grove Water Storage Company in the amount of $6350 that was broken down by: house, $600; wearing apparel, $300; ranch and well, $1000; one horse, $50; watches and jewelry, $300; general merchandise, $700; liquor

12. The names below are from Dr. Genung's account. "Suzie" may be a nickname for "Lydia." "Harry Cowell" is probably "Henry Cowell." Lydia and Henry were married on November 4, 1896 (Maricopa County marriage records). They are buried next to Henry Wickenburg in Wickenburg's Pioneer Cemetery.

and cigars, $150; farming implements, $100; corral, $50; two barns and lumber, $700; bar fixtures, $40; beds and bedding, $140; chickens, $50; hay and barley, $100; gold coin, $1200; gold dust, $100; sewing machine, $50; carpenter tools, $50; books and papers, $1000. Like many of the numbers in this story, the sum does not equal the reported total.

Mrs. Conger would later get her name in an eastern paper for saving the life of a man bitten by a rattlesnake near Smith's Mill[13] (*Washington Post*, Sept. 2, 1894, p. 7).

- Of 13 men in the bunkhouse near the Lower dam one resident had a desire for a bit of whiskey. When he reached for the bottle he heard a roar and shouted "My God, boys! The dam has broken! Run for your lives" (*Prescott Morning Courier*, Mar. 4). He reached high ground with the cork from the bottle still in his hand but did not get his drink (*Arizona Daily Gazette*, Mar. 7).

- Brill's farm was about three miles downstream from Wickenburg where the Hassayampa River Preserve (see map in Preface) is now located. Somehow his house was not destroyed, but his fruit trees were washed out or badly damaged and the field was three to four feet deep in sand and mud. Brill's foreman reported water of 25 feet deep (*Phoenix Daily Herald*, Feb. 24). "Every farm and ranch on the Hassayampa [was] destroyed except Brill's house. His orchard and vineyard [were] covered with sand" (*Arizona Daily Gazette*, Feb. 28). (Note the hydrograph, Figure 4-1, where

---

13. Smith's Mill was south of Seymour where W. C. Smith built a quartz mill for the Vulture Mine in 1873 (Granger, 1983, p. 571).

I have calculated the water depth at Brill's farm at about 28 feet.)

- Henry Wickenburg's ranch was destroyed. Nothing but a sand bar remained (*Phoenix Daily Herald*, Feb. 24). Wickenburg asked $7888 in the lawsuit (see the table on page 83 for all litigants).

- A safe was lost from Bob Brow's saloon[14]. It contained $4000 (*Phoenix Daily Herald*, Feb. 27), or $7000 (*Weekly Journal-Miner*, Feb.26; *San Francisco Chronicle*, Feb. 26), or $10,000 (*Arizona Daily Gazette*, Feb. 27). The hunt for the safe has been intense, even using metal detectors in more modern times, but it has not been found. The *Prescott Morning Courier* (Feb. 25) reported Brow missing, but he survived and went on to manage and later own the Palace Saloon on Whiskey Row in Prescott.

- Perhaps a 100 were left naked and starving along the Hassayampa (*Phoenix Daily Herald*, Feb. 24).

- From the *Prescott Weekly Journal-Miner* (Feb. 26):

  What the impetus of the stream of water was when once turned loose can be hardly appreciated without going over the ground covered by it. Those who saw it say that it came down in an almost perpendicular wall ninety or a hundred feet high, and apparently crushed down, instead of sweeping away, everything

---

14. According to Buchanan (2006), Bob Brow's saloon and Goodwin Station (where Dan Burke got drunk; see page 33) were the same. I believe Bob Brow's saloon was located at the Lower dam (Prescott *Journal-Miner*, Feb. 26, 1880; Willson, 1949)

before it. Immense boulders weighing tons were thrown around as a child might toss a ball, enormous trees were broken into sections or torn into shreds, iron bars were broken and twisted out of shape, and an ordinary flat-iron was picked up and carried five miles and then imbedded in the walls of the canyon.

- W. S. Colyer, Fred Hodder, and Jos. Reynolds were at a camp 100 yards downstream of the Lower dam (*Phoenix Daily Herald*, Feb. 24) or two miles downstream of the Lower dam (*Arizona Daily Gazette*, Feb. 27). The flood carried Colyer 75 yards downstream where he was caught in a whirlpool and shot up onto a bank, thus saved. Hodder also survived but Reynolds died. The water came to 75 feet deep where they were sleeping. (The flow calculations, Figure 4-1, put the maximum depth at the Lower dam at 65 feet.)

- L. D. Haynes' six-year-old daughter was found dead 35 miles downstream of the Lower dam.

- From the *San Francisco Chronicle* (Feb. 28, p. 3):

  F. M. Packer, the placer miner, lived about a mile below the dam. He has long hair, reaching away down on his shoulders, to which he says he owes his life. When the roof of his cabin, to which he was clinging, floated into the side of the hill his hair caught in some bushes, and, unlike Absalom, his long hair proved means of saving him instead of causing his death.

- One man was seen to start for a place of safety, and, seeing that escape was impossible, bravely turned his face to the flood to meet his fate. Nothing was ever seen of him after being struck by the water. Another man was seen going up a steep hill. He had reached a point about 15 feet above the level of the riverbank when the mighty volume of water struck and killed him (*San Francisco Chronicle*, Feb. 27, 1890, p. 6).

- The Vulture Mine lost five miles of pipeline valued at $20,000. That loss apparently caused a decrease in work. An article in the *Arizona Daily Gazette* of June 12, 1894 states: "It is said that a larger force of men will be put to work [at Vulture Mine] than there has been at any time since the pump line was broken by the Walnut Grove Flood."

- The dam burst at 1:45 am. Water reached the lower dam at 2:02 and was at Pipe Line City[15], six miles downstream of the lower dam, at 2:05 (*Arizona Daily Gazette*, Feb. 27). The flood reached the Gila River about 4:00 pm Saturday [Feb. 23] (*Phoenix Daily Herald*, Feb. 24).

- A teamster was killed at Smith's Mill (four miles downstream of Seymour) (*Arizona Daily Gazette*, Feb. 25). Man with a two-horse team swept away at Smith's Mill (*Phoenix Daily Herald*, Feb. 24).

- A steel boiler used at the Lower dam was found 30 miles downstream (*Arizona Daily Gazette*, Feb. 27).

- Ed Wiggins' arrastra and camp were destroyed but Ed was, fortunately, in Wickenburg (*Arizona Daily Gazette*, Feb. 24).

- John Hardee kept a saloon three miles below the Lower dam. Hardee, Ed Davis and Wm. Russell escaped by climbing a

---

15. I have never heard of Pipe Line City and the name does not appear in the books on historic place names in Arizona.

hillside (*Prescott Morning Courier*, Feb. 27). Hardee's story as told to the *Arizona Weekly Journal-Miner* (Mar. 5):

> I was located at the flume camp, between the lower dam and Headquarters. Our camp was situated on a bar of the creek. On the night of the disaster, myself and three others occupied a tent, retiring about ten o'clock at night. There was one man in bed with me. I was waked up towards morning by the roaring sound of the coming flood when I jumped out of bed and yelled to the boys to get up, that the dam had broken. All I had on was my underclothes. The others got up and we all started on a run for high ground. My pants and vest were under my pillow. In the former I had $166, and in the latter two fine gold watches, but I had no time to stop for either, and they were lost. We ran as fast as we could, but when we got about half-way up the hill I fell down and injured my leg. I ran on my hands and feet for quite a distance, the water crowding me all the time. When I fell, I looked back and saw a wave twenty feet high strike the tent. I finally got on my feet again and succeeded in reaching high ground above the line of the flood. At this point the valley is two hundred yards wide, and the water was sixty feet deep.

The first person I saw after getting out of the waters was Tom Boon[16], who is about 18 years old, who had his 8-year-old sister in his arms. Mrs. Boon soon came and said her husband and 14-year-old daughter had been lost. Mrs. Boon had a narrow escape, having been

---

16. Another account spells the name "Boone."

knocked down by the water. Mr. Boon awakened the family, and as the boy came to the door of their tent he saw his little sister, whom he immediately took in his arms and ran as fast as he could. Mr. Boon was the last one out of the tent, and, instead of starting direct[ly] for high ground, ran around the tent, presumably looking for the little girl, whom he had not seen.

The newspapers contain many more stories and anecdotes, some contradictory, some undoubtedly exaggerated and, perhaps, some true. In total they give a flavor of the devastation of the flood and of the human suffering caused by it.

All the newspapers were filled with the terrible discovery of mutilated bodies; dead hogs, cattle and horses; people naked or wearing feed sacks; litter consisting of parts of structures, bedding, personal possessions, machinery, broken wagons; and destroyed trees lining the river. Reports of bodies being discovered came in for weeks after the failure. Less reported, but implied, was the change in the river, especially in the vicinity of Wickenburg, that pretty well wiped out agriculture and gold processing along the river forever. Henry Wickenburg's farm essentially disappeared, as did most of the agricultural lands along the banks of the river. The flood reportedly scoured the channel clear of riparian vegetation to the Gila River (Webb, 2007, p. 329). The changes the flood made in the river are not known precisely. For more on the effects of large floods, see information on the flood of 1970 (page 88).

Dam Safety

The Johnstown flood (May 31, 1889) was a monumental disaster. One would expect that such an event would inflame the nation and prompt congressional action. The Walnut Grove Dam failure, less than nine months later, should have added emphasis and urgency. Reaction to these events seems muted compared to latter-day disasters. Perhaps the reason was that these events did not appear on a screen in living rooms at the time; indeed, Marconi did not send his message by radio across the Atlantic until 1901. The only source of news for the citizenry was the newspaper, although the papers did have the advantage of telegraph.

It is understandable that those in the East would pay little attention to western events. The West was alien territory; it might as well have been on the other side of the planet. Both the Johnstown flood and the Walnut Grove Dam collapse did get attention in Congress, but they did not lead to much-needed dam-safety legislation. A search of the U.S. Congressional Series Set produces mention of the Walnut Grove Dam in the following (numbers in parentheses are the numbers of the Series Set):

—Capt. C. E. Dutton, Chief Engineer, U. S. Irrigation Survey, March 11, 1890
—J. W. Gregory, Feb. 11, 1891 (2888) and 1899 (3767)
—1892 pictures folder (2937 and 3092)
—A short description of the dam, Feb. 7, 1896 (3456) and June 1, 1896 (3465)

Apparently, there was a bill that in some respect treated dam safety:

> The provisions of this bill ... provide for the most thorough, systematic, and authoritative inspection of all dams, reservoirs, and other irrigation works, with a view to preventing such horrors and the breaking

of the South Fork dam, the Walnut Grove Dam, and other things of the same kind, growing out of reck-lessness, carelessness and cupidity.

There is no evidence that such a bill became law. Congress did pass the "General Dam Act" in 1906, but it did not treat dam safety.

Arizona became worried about the impending construction of Hoover Dam and passed a dam safety act in 1929. The act pro-vided for review of the plans and the inspection of construc-tion. It has been revised and carried forward in subsequent years. The application and fee structure can be found on the Internet.

The first federal dam safety act was signed by President Nixon on August 9, 1972. A second dam safety act was signed by Pres-ident Carter on November 2, 1978, following five major fail-ures in the 1970s. They were (Association of State Dam Safety Officials):

—February 26, 1972: Buffalo Creek Valley, West Virginia–125 lives, $400 million in damages
—June 9, 1972: Rapid City, South Dakota–33 to 237 lives, $60 million in damages
—June 5, 1976: Teton, Idaho–11 lives, $1 billion in damages
—July 19-20, 1977: Laurel Run, Pennsylvania–40 lives, $5.3 million in damages.
—November 5, 1977: Toccoa Falls, Georgia–39 lives, $2.5 mil-lion in damages.

By September 1981 the U. S. Army Corp of Engineers had inspected 8639 dams, one-third of which were declared unsafe. In 82% of the cases the primary defect was inadequate spillway capacity (Costa, 1988, p. 439). Recently the ASDSO reported that 3361 U. S. dams have hydraulic or structural deficiencies.

Additional dam safety acts have followed, but it seems that the federal government was late to the starting line on dam safety. It has often been said that a catastrophe is required to get Congress to act; two dam catastrophes did not move them, but five later ones did. The Association of State Dam Safety Officials has a list of U. S. dam failures beginning in 1874[17].

---

17. http://www.damsafety.org/news/?p=94bdfdd0-633a-4fa2-bc390083c58d14ba

Chapter 5: The dam

Construction of Walnut Grove Dam proceeded with fits and starts but was completed fairly quickly. It was started by Prof. Blake in 1886 and completed late in 1888 (see Appendix I: Timeline). In less than two years there were five "engineers" in charge of the construction plus about a month in which the contractor worked with no supervising engineer. After failure that left a number of people who could be blamed for the disaster.

Engineers

Most of those in charge of building the dam carried the title "Chief Engineer and Superintendent." The first, Prof. Blake, had no engineering education or experience but was the original designer of the dam. The fact that there were five engineers and a contractor in charge of design and construction from August, 1886, to completion in December, 1888, seems to indicate a general dissatisfaction with the working conditions.

Prof. William P. Blake

Almost all references to Blake refer to him as "Professor Blake"; he was first professor at the College of California from 1864 to 1867, where the majority of his time was spent setting up a school of mining and agriculture. In 1867 the College of California was absorbed, without Blake, into the new University of

California, Burns Ranch Campus (later Berkeley) (Dill, 1991). Blake at the age of 69 joined the University of Arizona—established in 1885—in 1895 where he began a school of mining and metallurgy. He remained an active professor until 1905.

Figure 5-1. William Phipps Blake (from Raymond, 1911)

Blake's specialty was mineralogy, receiving his degree from Yale University in 1852. His early consulting was in the eastern part of the United States but later he concentrated in the western part of North America. Blake was a world traveler, spending a couple of years in Japan and making several trips to Europe. Blake had two sons, Frank and Whitney, who were also employed for a time on the dam. A great deal about Blake is known because of the extensive diaries and papers that he left, which are now available at the Arizona Historical Society

Museum in Tucson, and because of his extremely prolific writing. Raymond (1911) has a list of his papers. Blake and Wagoner (page 54) were two scientific superstars[1] who had major roles to play in the design and construction of Walnut Grove Dam. Unfortunately, Blake's expertise was not in engineering; a review of his publications shows nothing in that subject. Both terminated their service with the Walnut Grove Water Storage Company on a sour note. Dill (1991) has a biographical article on Blake.

Dillingham and Newberry hired Prof. Blake to assess the feasibility of hydraulic mining in the vicinity of Antelope Creek, Weaver Creek and the Hassayampa River. Upon giving a favorable report, Blake was hired to begin construction on the dam, appointed director of the Walnut Grove Water Storage Company and appointed president of the Piedmont Cattle Company (the company formed by the financiers for irrigation, see page 8). His employment with the WGWSC netted him a salary of $500 per month and a title of Chief Engineer and Superintendent. Blake's son, Frank, was 26 years old when surveying and the initial work on the dam was begun; he earned a civil engineering degree in 1886 but is listed in the 1920 census as a mining engineer. None of the Blakes had any dam-building experience. Given this situation I can't be certain who did the initial design; it was probably some combination of the old man and his sons.

---

1. As an interesting side note, Blake developed an exhibit classification system for the 1876 Centennial Exposition in Philadelphia that "had a sound scientific basis. ... It is designed to carry the spectator through the successive steps of human progress..." (*New York Times*, Mar. 4, 1876, p. 2). Then, according to Maass (1972): "Melvil Dewey patterned his decimal classification system after the one developed by William Phipps Blake for the Philadelphia Centennial Exhibition of 1876." Thus, it seems that Blake invented the "Dewey decimal system," still used to classify library books.

In all references to the design in the engineering literature, it is attributed to Prof. Blake.

In the 19th century an educated person could obtain at least a superficial knowledge in any field[2]. As an acclaimed geologist with a long and distinguished history in mining and consulting, Blake undoubtedly was confident of his ability to design and construct a dam even though he had no engineering education or experience. Blake first began an evaluation of the area with Wells Bates. After finding a satisfactory amount of gold in the placer deposits of Antelope Creek, Weaver Creek and the Hassayampa, he located the dam site on the property of Judge Abner Wade and acquired the right to construct a dam up to 60 feet high at the site (Dill, 1987, p. 288).

Although the agreement between the WGWSC and Wade was for a dam 60 feet high, in late December, 1886, Blake told ex-Governor Frederick A. Tritle, who visited the camp, that the dam would be 80 or more feet high (Dill, 1987, p. 288). Later the dam was redesigned by E. N. Robinson (page 51) to a height of 110 feet, at that time the highest dam in the United States (Moritz, 1945, p. 2).

Initial surveying began August 10, 1886, and by late December the foundation wall had reached 30 feet high. Blake's relationship with Dillingham and Bates must have been rocky from shortly after the start of the dam. After only five months from the beginning of Blake's surveys, he was fired and replaced by E. N. Robinson, who redesigned the dam. I can only surmise that

2. That ability may have disappeared with Einstein. Those educated in science could understand the theory of relativity on a superficial basis, but since Einstein had to invent new mathematics to describe the theory, even mathematicians of the early 20th century were unable to perform calculations.

the officials of the Walnut Grove Water Storage Company rec-ognized—or hired a consultant (perhaps Robinson, see page 51) who recognized—deficiencies in Blake's design and construc-tion. The only indication in the literature that his dismissal was due to ineptitude is Blake's own statement (quoted below).

Blake may have left the design and construction in some disarray. According to Wagoner (1888), "Blake carried a wall across the cañon to bed rock through about 20 feet of sand and gravel. What his intentions were to do next is not known, as no records were made or kept by the company's officers at the dam."[3]

Blake's dismissal by Dillingham—coupled with a lack of pay-ment for what, in his opinion, was his due and the lack of cred-it for his accomplishments—was extremely upsetting to him. He claimed to be a pioneer in the project who saw it through its most difficult phase and yet was dismissed without reason. His diaries are critical of Dillingham and the Bates brothers. Dill (1987) quotes Blake referring to Dillingham and Bates: "their game is to steal away all my interest in both corporations under the pretense that I did not build, or start, the dam properly! Vil-lains!" Yet given what is known about Blake's design and con-struction, detailed subsequently, his dismissal was more than justified. Unfortunately, those who followed fared little better.

Blake brought suit against the Walnut Grove Water Storage Company in October 1887, in Yavapai District Court to recover salary owed to him in the amount of $4000 plus interest of 10%

---

3. Although some of the company's records may have been located at the Lower dam and lost in the flood there was no reason that design drawings and like material for the main dam would be there. Note that Wagoner's statement was written before the dam collapsed when records should have been available.

per year⁴. The case was "amicably settled by and between the parties thereto by payment by Defendant to Plaintiff of the claim and demand for the collection of which action was brought" on February 6, 1888.

Edwin N. Robinson

Robinson was a civil engineer from San Francisco. Wilson (1893) states: "Col. E. N. Robinson ..., who succeeded Prof. Blake as chief engineer, had constructed several dams of the same kind in California which have successfully withstood the floods of a quarter of a century." Robinson redesigned Blake's dam, raising the height to 110 feet. Wagoner (1988) says of Robinson, "I presume that the cross-sections and general methods of construction were fixed by Mr. Robinson. Under him the dam was commenced in the rear of the Blake wall, apparently making a part of Blake's construction useless, and was described in the specifications as being composed of front and back walls 14 feet at the base and 4 feet at the top, with loose rock filling between." Lester Robinson, Edwin's son, in a letter to the *San Francisco Chronicle* (Feb. 28, 1890, p. 3) says that Blake's wall "leaked considerably, fish seven inches long being known to have passed through in some way, and the water had so thoroughly undermined this portion of the work that the new dam was commenced just back of the Blake wall." Wagoner gives a good description of the dam (see the section on design, page 58).

Also, Robinson proposed constructing a spillway 55 feet wide and 12 feet deep. The location of the proposed spillway is in some doubt. Dill (1981) puts it one-half mile east of the dam;

---

4. Case number 1500. The case records are available on film at the Arizona State Library and Archives in Phoenix.

Wilson (1893) puts it one-half mile north of the dam; Brodie (see page 135) indicates that it would have passed from the reservoir to Cottonwood Creek[5], which is west of the dam. Although I believe Brodie was incorrect on other aspects of the spillway, his location is the most logical. There is a saddle just over 3400 feet msl west of the dam through which a spillway could have been cut for modest cost.

In April of 1887, less than four months after he had been hired, Robinson was fired. I cannot determine the reason, but surmise that he proposed expensive fixes to the structure, including his spillway, that the owners did not want to pay for; or, perhaps he was the victim of one or more of the Bates brothers. In any case the circumstances were bizarre. After the collapse Robinson was criticized in the press. As he was in Europe at the time, his son, Lester L. Robinson (about 17 years old in 1890), published a letter in his defense (*San Francisco Chronicle*, Feb. 28, 1890, p. 3) in which he stated:

> He received letters two days before [his dismissal] from both Mr. Dillingham, the president of the company, and Mr. Newberry, also an officer of the company, commending him on the good work being done and his first knowledge of removal came from an assistant engineer who overheard some talk on the subject; so he quietly gathered together all his private papers and went to his house.
>
> Sometime between 8 p.m. and the next morning young [Walter] Bates (see the next section, page 53) and his assistant forced their way into the office and

---

5. The court records mention Ash Creek or Willow Creek, neither of which is in the vicinity of the dam.

took possession. Mr. Robinson did not hear from them of his removal until 9:30 o'clock that morning, and he never received a word from the company until the following day, when a telegram came announcing the fact. I believe that the telegram was a false one, for after he went to New York to settle with the company he was earnestly requested to once more take charge of the work, but he respectfully declined.

However, Robinson was never paid by the Walnut Grove Water Storage Company. Lester Robinson's letter continues:

Mr. Robinson did not leave Arizona immediately after his retirement ... but remained three or four months, when he went back to New York to make a settlement with the company. He, however, did not make a satisfactory settlement and has not to this day, as they had not the money to pay what was due him.

John Currier, Robinson's assistant, remained for only two weeks after Robinson's resignation. In a letter (*San Francisco Chronicle*, Feb. 26, 1890, p. 3) he wrote:

[It was impossible] to exact good work, and it was of more importance to float bonds and sell stock on Wall Street, New York, than to construct a substantial dam, as I was quietly given to understand by Major Dake, a friend of Well[s] H. Bates, the resident director, with large blocks of stock.

About May 1887, the work became so disgraceful [that] I quietly determined to leave. At this time, I was superintendent of construction, appointed by the contractor and approved by the board of directors in New York.

Further, Currier attributes bad work as one reason that Robinson left the company (see page 73).

Walter G. Bates

Walter Bates replaced Robinson as superintendent of construction. He was only 27 years old[6] at the time and a younger brother of Wells and DeWitt. Bates apparently had no engineering credentials. I believe that he became a salesman.

Walter Bates wrote an article in Scribner's Magazine (1890, pp. 3–17)—ironically published in January, 1890, just before the dam collapsed—in which he discusses agriculture in the West and the need to store water for irrigation. Although the article is not entirely about Arizona or Walnut Grove Dam, he describes the project and includes several pictures. A large part is devoted to the difficulties encountered in construction, including the transportation of materials, the need to set up an entire town, and, especially, labor difficulties. In the latter category he complains: "[The laborers] work when they choose and lay off in the same way. A pay-day sees saloons and gambling-houses in full blast, and but little work is forthcoming for a week. ... In the Southwest this labor must be largely Mexican, now that public opinion prevents the employment of Chinese. If not Mexican then it must be the scarce, highly paid, independent white labor of the West." Bates' experience and frustration as superintendent are evident.

---

6. Dill (1987, p. 292) puts his age at 21, which he probably got from a letter to the *San Francisco Chronicle* (Feb. 28, 1890, p. 3) from Lester L. Robinson. The U. S. census 1870-1910 indicates that he was 27. Dill does not specify that Walter was related to Wells and DeWitt.

In view of the fate of the dam, his statement about the necessary skills is prophetic: "The building of a great dam anywhere is a most difficult task, involving the best, and often the boldest, engineering skill, great administration ability, and the most scrupulous fidelity in minute details."

Luther Wagoner

Luther Wagoner was another of the San Francisco engineers. His many publications and the citations to those papers yield much information about his professional activities and competence. His résumé is truly impressive. He was an expert and designer of dams of all types and his was one of the first analyses of arch dams. Wagoner was proficient in mathematics, not a common skill of 19th century engineers. He did experiments in fluid mechanics including measuring the speed of falling objects in water and glycerin, calibrating weirs and analyzing open channel flow. Wagoner was instrumental in the design of harbor facilities in San Francisco bay, before which he traveled around the United States and Europe to obtain information (Wagoner and Heuer, 1908). Part of his harbor design was devising a method to prevent deterioration of wood piers by marine borers.

Wagoner was a licensed land surveyor. He located dam sites in the California Sierras, one of which was Hetch-Hetchy, the present-day source of San Francisco's water supply[7]. He invented a method to find minute amounts of gold and silver and applied it

---

7. I hope that environmentalist do not hold that against Wagoner. The HetchHetchy Valley is claimed to be as magnificent as its neighbor, Yosemite, but its scenic wonders remain submerged. California required land surveyors to be licensed in 1891, but civil engineers were not required to have a license until 1929 following the failure of St. Francis Dam.

to quantify the amount of gold in sea water, citations to that paper appearing long after his death. He was also accomplished in geology and forestry. Wagoner was a truly amazing man of his time.

He began work at Walnut Grove Dam on August 10, 1887. His primary duty was to survey and design a 19-mile flume from the dam site to the placer beds (see page 132). Wagoner (*Engineering News*, Apr. 5, 1890, p. 328) confirms that "I was engaged in surveying a flume line, but I periodically inspected progress of the work [at the main dam] at least once a week until completion."

Wagoner wrote extensively about the dam and was very critical of it *before* failure (Wagoner, 1888, p. 73) writing that "The history of the construction of the dam is one full of blunders, mainly caused by officers of the company in New York" (see also the *San Francisco Chronicle*, Feb. 24, 1890, p. 1).

James Emmett Anderson

Of the "engineers" who worked on the dam, the most obscure and unknown is Anderson. He was appointed chief engineer in the fall of 1887 as the dam was nearing completion.

Alexander Oswald Brodie

Brodie (Figure 5-2, Figure 5-3) was the last and the most famous of all the engineers. He attended St. Lawrence University and graduated from the United States Military Academy at West Point in 1870. After serving in the army—mostly in the West—he resigned in 1877. He appeared in the Arizona Territory about 1883 but was not there for more than six months until 1887 or 1888. He was assistant engineer on the Walnut Grove Dam in 1888-89. After a short time away from that project, he returned as Chief Engineer and Superintendent in September, 1889. By that time the dam was essentially finished, although Brodie undertook an enlargement of the spillway in December of 1889. His primary attention was focused on the construction of the Lower (diversion) dam and the flume from there to the placer deposits.

Although Brodie was chief engineer at the time of failure, he was not held responsible. He sometimes signed himself as "civil engineer," but there is nothing in his biography that I have read that leads me to believe that he acquired engineering experience before this connection with the Walnut Grove Water Storage Company. My assessment is that Brodie was a good leader and organizer—a common quality of those with a military education—but lacked the engineering skills and experience to lead a project as complex as dam construction.

Alexander Oswald Brodie
1st U.S. Cavalry

Figure 5-2. Probably Brodie's graduation picture from West Point. This is the only picture that I have found in which he doesn't have a mustache.

Courtesy of the Arizona State Archives

Figure 5-3. Governor Brodie

The most colorful aspects of Brodie's life occurred after the dam failure. He became involved in various mining ventures in central Arizona, primarily the Crown Point Mine. When war with Spain loomed in 1897 Brodie, with the assistance of William Owen ("Buckey") O'Neill (see page 35), organized a group of volunteers for the Arizona squadron of the Rough Riders. He served in Cuba where he was wounded, and O'Neill was killed at San Juan. Brodie was appointed Arizona Territorial Governor July 1, 1902, and served until he resigned on February 14, 1905, to return to the military.

In December of 1892 Brodie married his second wife (his first died in childbirth early in their marriage), Mary Hanlon (see page 37), who was the niece of Van Beuren and a "heroine" of the flood from the dam failure.

Design

There is little written about the early design. Blake had a crude drawing in one of his diaries. It simply shows a downstream slope of 54° from horizontal, and upstream slope of 60°, a bottom width of 115 feet and a top width that appears to be 27 feet. (He actually has "12+15", which, I think, is 6 feet of rock facing on both sides surrounding 15 feet of rock fill; however, that is much wider than the eventual result.) Both the upstream and downstream faces are clad in hand-placed rock. I do not know if Blake produced working drawings or simply began directing the construction from such sketches. Certainly, he had little time to make design drawings and his diaries, at least those that I have seen, do not refer to definite plans. If indeed Blake began construction with only rough sketches, that attests to his incompetence as an engineer and his extreme naivety in engineering construction.

On January 12, 1887, about the time that Blake was fired, the Walnut Grove Water Storage Company signed a contract with the San Francisco construction firm of Nagel and Leonard. The "Plans and Specifications" for the dam were attached to that contract. These plans are reproduced in full in Appendix IV. They describe in a sketch the basic dimensions of the dam and the type of construction. The details are left to the "engineer in charge." The plans contain no calculation or rationale for the design, not even a computation on basic dam stability or the stability of the rock slopes on the upstream and downstream sides. There is no mention of a spillway in either the contract or the plans. Neither is the culvert under the dam mentioned or shown on the sketch. Apparently, Robinson, appointed chief engineer and superintendent at that time, was to build the dam on an ad-hoc basis as the construction proceeded. The paucity of planning makes the firing of Robinson four months later and the hiring of a non-engineer, Walter Bates, especially relevant.

Descriptions of the near-completed and completed dam are presented in *Engineering News* (Oct. 20, 1888, pp. 303–304), Wagoner (1888), Schuyler (1901, pp. 58–63; 1909, pp. 53–58) and Dill (1987). Much of the Schuyler description comes from Wagoner. In addition, there are six photographs taken by J. I. Gardner[8] of Prescott and rescued by John Cooper of Cooper's Ranch, now on the Abner Wade homestead (see Burden, 2004, pp. iii–iv and pp. 128–133).

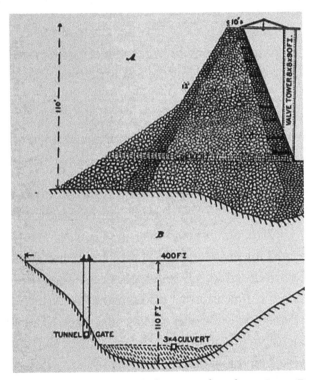

Figure 5-4. The cross-section and elevation of Walnut Grove Dam (from Wagoner (1888, pp. 77–78), Schuyler (1901, p. 59; 1909, p. 54) and U.S. Congressional Series Set 3092).

---

8. Those knowledgeable about Prescott will know that J. I. Gardner owned the Gardner Mercantile on North Cortez Street. The business was in the same location from the 1880s to the 1950s. The building is now the home of Murphy's Restaurant.

The dam dimensions were (see Figure 5-4):

> Length = 400 feet at top, length at base = 150 feet
> Width at base = 138 feet, width at top = 10 feet
> Height = 110 feet

Figure 5-5. The nearly completed dam looking upstream (from Schuyler, 1901, p. 55). Note that the flume (page 63) is running water and that the spillway (left side of picture) enters the river at the toe of the dam.

The nearly completed dam appears in Figure 5-5. *Engineering News* of October 20, 1888, shows some details of the dam (Figure 5-6).

Although rockfill dam construction was newer than earthen or concrete gravity dams, the Walnut Grove Dam had several predecessors, mostly in California. The idea was to construct an economical dam in locations where transportation was difficult and to use locally available materials. The principle, as in all gravity dams, is the provision of a barrier heavy enough so that it is not pushed downstream and wide enough so that it cannot be tipped by the water in the impoundment.

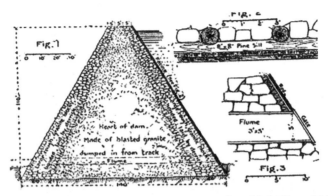

Figure 5-6. Details of the dam (*Engineering News*, Oct. 20, 1888, p. 304). The flume dimensions are given as 3 feet by 5 feet.

Arch dams, those designed to withstand the force of the water by the structural strength of concrete, were to come later.

The most common use for the rockfill dam was that of the Walnut Grove Dam, hydraulic mining. Thus, the dam was often considered temporary and to be taken down when it was no longer needed. A subset of the rockfill type dam is the crib dam where wooden boxes were filled with rock and stacked to form the dam. These were nearly always temporary because the rotting wood released the rocks so that eventually the dam failed.

Walnut Grove Dam consisted of a pile of rock, blasted from the hillside, and dumped randomly. That pile was faced with hand-placed rock on both the water side and the downstream side. A challenge for this type of construction is the sealing of the dam. Schuyler (1909, pp. 1-2) list several methods of sealing: central steel plates protected by asphalt or concrete, steel plate supported by I-beams on the dam face, masonry or reinforced concrete on the face, an earth face, earth hydraulically placed to fill the voids in the rock or a wooden facing sealed with caulk and tar paper. Walnut Grove Dam used the last method. It consisted of cedar logs eight to ten inches in diameter placed into the water face. Vertical stringers of native pine four feet apart were bolted to the logs. These formed the structure to support a double planking of three-inch boards with tar paper between the boards. The outer boards were caulked with oakum and painted with paraffin paint. Concrete was used to seal the boards to the bedrock at the base.

This effort to seal the dam appears to be sufficient, but in my opinion there is one flaw: The loose rock forming the dam is bound to settle over time. That settlement will place great stress on the wood and crack it—thus tearing the tar paper and the caulk—allowing water to enter. See the section on leaks on page 68.

All dams, except those specifically designed as overflow structures, must be provided with a spillway to pass flood water past the dam. There is virtually no dam that has outlet works of sufficient capacity to handle floods. The outlet works of the Walnut Grove Dam consisted of two twenty-inch pipes a bit above the base of the dam with a capacity to pass an amount of water at least two orders of magnitude (factor of 100) less than the flood flow. (See also the section on the mysterious flume, page 63.) That leaves the question of how big the spillway should be. To answer that question, the designer must know or assume how large a flood flow can be expected and the shape of the hydrograph, a plot of flow versus time.

In the case of the Walnut Grove Dam there was no hydrographic survey to determine how much flow would, or could, pass down the Hassayampa River. In fact, the designers had only a rough estimate of the drainage area and I could find nowhere in the early literature that they bothered to look up rainfall records.[9] Wagoner did estimate historical flood flows from high water marks below the dam, but that was after the dam was almost finished. Neither in the literature did I find a calculation of the capacity of the spillway that was finally designed. Thus, all of those involved in design were apparently negligent in providing adequate flood protection.

The design of a spillway is not a trivial matter, *especially if it is close to the dam*. Obviously, the spillway should be large enough to pass floods. It should be built so that it does not erode under the (usually) high speed flow of the water descending from the level of a full lake to the riverbed below the dam[10]. If it is near the dam, the erosive power of the water must be directed so that it doesn't compromise the structure. Robinson, the engineer who redesigned Blake's dam, designed a spillway at a remote point (see page 52), but the owners rejected that option for unknown reasons but probably because it cost too much. The spillway that was initially built was in the west canyon wall almost adjacent to the dam and had its downstream terminus almost against the dam's toe (see the photograph, Figure 5-5). The capacity of that spillway was grossly inadequate by a large margin (see the section on river flow in Appendix II, page 121).

---

9. Apparently, the only rainfall records available were those taken at Fort Whipple, about five miles north of Prescott and outside of the Hassayampa River watershed. Even so, they would have been better than nothing.

10. The erosion of a spillway may be more severe than expected. In 1983 a flood at Glen Canyon Dam took out three feet of reinforced concrete and a very large amount of bedrock from the left spillway. The spillway was saved by shutting down the water through the placement of temporary barriers. It is a lesson that destruction by fast-flowing water should not be underestimated.

Moreover, its placement—which was never commented on in the engineering literature either before or after failure—foretold the fate of Walnut Grove Dam.

Construction

The construction of Walnut Grove Dam consisted primarily of blasting rock from the canyon wall, hauling it to the dam and onto a trestle in mine cars and dumping it (see Figure 5-7). The facing on both sides of the embankment consisted of rock that was levered into place. No gradation or compaction was done. As the dam reached the level of the trestle, the trestle was raised, leaving the supporting columns in the dam.

The foundation of the dam was designed to be on bedrock, under the thick layer of sand that usually constitutes the bed of the river. Whether or not it was on bedrock for the length of the dam is a matter of controversy.

The Mysterious Flume

A box culvert, made of wood, was placed beneath the dam at the elevation of the stream bed (see Figure 5-9, Figure 5-4 and Figure 5-5). Different dimensions of this flume appear in the various publications about the dam and even in diagrams of the construction:

—*Engineering News* (Oct. 20, 1888, p. 304): 3 feet wide by 5 feet
—Wagoner (1888): 3 feet by 4 feet
—Wilson (1893, quoting Wagoner, 1888): 3 feet by 4 feet
—*Engineering News* (Mar. 1, 1890, p. 206; Mar. 8, 1890, p. 229): 5 feet square

Figure 5-7. The dam under construction (from Bates, 1890, p. 6). The flume, under construction, emerges from the bottom center of the dam. The intake tower is shown on the left. Mine cars that haul rock from the quarry are at the top of the trestle.

The calculations of Appendix II (see page 128) used the dimensions of 3 feet by 5 feet for reasons explained therein. The calculations are meant to determine what role the flume might have had in the failure of the dam if it had been open.

I am not the first to wonder about the role of the flume. Schuyler (1909, p. 58) states:

> None of the published descriptions of the construction have stated what disposition was made of the culvert under the center of the dam at the streambed, after construction was finished, or whether it was walled up or merely closed by a wooden gate.

Figure 5-8. The nearly completed dam looking eastward (*Engineering News*, Oct. 20, 1888, p. 303). The spillway is out of the picture at the near end. The article does not list an author, but it does attribute the photograph to "Bates Bros., bankers of this city [New York], and the original projectors of the enterprise."

Engineering News (March 8, 1890, p. 229) assumed that the purpose of the flume was to evacuate water from the reservoir. It says:

> We are now positively informed, by undoubt-
> ed authority, that the gate to the 5 ft. square flume
> through the dam has been jammed and immovable for
> months; and as a consequence this important safety-
> valve in case of floods was utterly useless, and could
> not be opened immediately preceding the disaster.
> This jamming of the valve, or gate, is not to be won-
> dered at when we learn that it was made of wood,
> sliding on wood, with 15 sq. ft. of surface in contact.
> The only provision for opening it was a 6 in. square
> wooden rod running up outside of the water face of
> the dam, with what is reported, and so seems from the
> photographs, as a very inadequate lifting appliance.
> Taking into account the effect of any settlement in
> jamming the guides, and a pressure of over 30 tons on

the slides of the gate alone, it is not remarkable that the gate could not be opened when needed.

Further in the same article:

> If Mr. Thomas Brown had judiciously used some of his dynamite in breaking up the gate of the 5 ft. conduit, he would have very materially assisted his waste-weir in getting rid of the flood-water, and might probably have saved the dam, and the lives and property that it destroyed.

Figure 5-9. The flume as it emerges from the dam (after Bates, 1890, p. 8). The caption to Bates' picture is: "Beginning of a Flume at Walnut Grove."

I wish that I were able to ask the editor of *Engineering News* how he expected Mr. Brown to place the dynamite at a depth of 110 feet during a flood and ignite it. Moreover, I disagree that opening the flume would "probably have saved the dam" (page 128).

The pull to open the gate, if it was not jammed, with 100 feet of water in reservoir would have been in the neighborhood of 764 lbs., and that assumes that there was no obstruction such as swelling of wood. Although mention of a lifting mechanism appears above, I do not know of such a device. The lifting force would have been applied by workmen pulling on the rod. I do not believe that this flume was ever intended to evacuate flood water.

Since the original purpose of the dam was to supply water to the placer operations of Antelope Creek and Weaver Creek, the flume was apparently intended to carry water from the dam to those operations. In Brodie's letter to Van Beuren (see page 132) he states that Wagoner was "given solely charge of the survey for a flume line 19 miles in length from the dam to Fools Creek" when he took over as chief engineer on Aug. 10, 1887.

Such an undertaking is regarded as foolish. First, the difficulty with the gate as outlined above is even more applicable to the delivery of water to the flume as the gate would have to be manipulated to obtain the correct amount of water. Should it hang in the open position one can only imagine the problems that would ensue at the lower end having a large flow with 300 feet or more of head.

Near the dam the head in the flume might have reached nearly 100 feet, depending on the depth of the reservoir and the velocity of the water. For a five-foot high box, that would mean that more than 30,000 pounds of outward force would be applied to every foot of length. An extensive and expensive structure would be necessary. Any major deflections in the structure would lead to leaks that would be very difficult to handle, might represent substantial water loss and would be impossible to repair while the flume contained water. Bursting of the flume would drain the lake, or most of it, before the flow could be stopped by closing the inadequate gate in the reservoir.

These problems must have been recognized after the flume was placed in the dam but before it was extended any distance downstream. Brodie's report (see page 133) states: "In the fall of 1888 further work was projected by the Company and Mr. Anderson was sent down the canyon, 14 miles below the reservoir to construct a small service dam with a flume line 5 miles long to carry a head of 1,200 inches of water to the gravel deposits below." Thus, the idea of a 19-mile flume was replaced by the construction of the Lower dam (25 feet high)[11] and a flume 5 miles in length to the placer sites. One is left to wonder who was instrumental in abandoning the idea and why Blake, Bates, Robinson and Wagoner did not realize that the original flume could not work.

Leaks

The completed Walnut Grove Dam leaked badly. Schuyler (1901, p. 76) quotes Wagoner (1888) as saying: "With 70 feet of water above bed-rock the dam leaked 3.75 cubic feet per second[12] [1683

---

11. Brodie puts the dimensions of the Lower dam as 45 feet thick at the bottom, 44.5 feet high, 220 feet long and 10 feet wide at the top (Appendix III).

12. Wagoner (1888, p. 76) actually said "...the dam leaked 141 inches (1.6 cu. ft.=1 inch.)" Schuyler interpreted this number as 141 x 1.6 / 60 = 3.75. Wagoner was using a "miner's inch," a measure of streamflow. The miner's inch was variously defined from 1.2 cubic feet per minute to 1.56 cubic feet per minute in the U. S. In New Zealand it was used as 60 cubic feet per minute. For an explanation of the methods of measurement and the uncertainty in a miner's inch see Bowie (1885, p. 121). Bowie begins by stating: "The miner's inch of water is a quantity which varies in almost every district in California."

gallons per minute][13]." Now *any* leak in an earth dam is cause for alarm; it is a rapidly growing cancer that can destroy the dam in short order. Measures must be taken to plug the leak while the lake is drained so that a permanent fix can be made.

A leak in a rockfill dam may or may not be serious[14]. It is like an unknown noise in the engine of your car, a cause for concern but not necessarily something that indicates imminent failure. In this case it was certainly something not designed into the structure and a fault that should have required investigation to determine if it indicated a serious structural problem that could grow to be of major importance. Nevertheless, Blake (1889) in a talk before the American Institute of Mining Engineers made light of the leak:

> As to the effect upon the stream below, there has been an agreeable surprise. Either from a partial opening of one of the gates or a leak, there has been a constant flow of water from the dam; and this has kept a constant stream through the valley, giving more water than usual along its course, so that instead of the owners of water-privileges denouncing the dam and asking for injunctions, they are hoping that the dam will always leak to their advantage.

Amazing! If you took your car to a mechanic to analyze the noise in the engine and the mechanic brushed it off saying that you are

---

13. Wilson (1893) said, "With 70 feet of water above the bed rock the dam leaked nearly 3 second-feet [i.e., cubic feet per second, cfs]."

14. The rockfill Chatswood dam in Colorado leaked badly without serious consequence; however, it was repaired (Schuyler,1909, p. 42). Leakage is believed to be the cause of failure of the Lake Avalon dam on the Pecos River in 1904.

lucky to be able to hear the engine better, you would surely be looking for another mechanic. Blake's statement, made by the original designer of the dam, speaks about his competence as an engineer, indicating that he should have stuck to geology. Schuyler (1909, p. 58) quotes the Blake statement and then says:

> It is remarkable that the designer of this dam should have looked upon the really enormous leakage developed in it in a spirit of exultation, as an achievement worthy of note, rather than as a source of alarm and danger. To write of such leakage as one of the results "of great value" requires unusual confidence in the stability of one's work.

Wagoner (1888, p. 76) speculates as to the cause of the leak:

> Various theories were advanced for the cause of the leak: one was, that settlement of the dam had forced an opening of the junction of the inclined and horizontal skins; and another was, that it leaked all over the whole surface. The extreme right hand skin below the bed of the stream ... is made of but one plank. The machinery for draining the water was inadequate, and the men who did the cementing to bed rock assured me that they worked in four feet of water[15], and that they did not go to bed rock, while per contra the sub-contractor ... for the work assured me it was well done. The probable cause of leakage, I believe, is all three of the reasons named.

---

15. Currier denied that men worked in four feet of water (*San Francisco Chronicle*, Feb. 26, 1890, p. 6).

I basically agree with Wagoner. Court testimony after the failure indicated that the dam did not extend to bedrock at the upstream part; thus, the leak could have originated in the sand under the dam and flowed through the rock fill. The inevitable settling of the rock fill probably ruptured the carefully laid waterproofing timbers and tar paper. The latter reason may not have been critical to the safety of the dam, but the former could have indicated a structural flaw.

The Spillway

The date was March 17, 1889. The Hassayampa River was in flood. Water was rising rapidly behind the Walnut Grove Dam and reached a level of only one foot below the crest. The spillway ran for the first time, but was clogged by debris, primarily trees and limbs that had floated down the river or originated from uncleared timber in the reservoir. Although Dill (1987, p. 294) states that Abner Wade's house was washed away, the *Arizona Weekly Journal-Miner* (Mar. 5, 1890) reported that just prior to the dam failure "the water was four feet higher at Judge Abner Wade's place than during the last flood, coming up to the floor of his residence," implying that his house was not lost in the March high water.[16] A large amount of lumber was lost at the Lower dam, then under construction (Dill, 1987, p. 294; Bates quotation, *Engineering News*, Apr. 26, 1890, p. 390). Blasting cleared the spillway and the water slowly began to recede; the

---

16. Many of the numbers cited in various publications do not agree, but they do in this case. The water was one foot under the crest of the dam in 1889 and overtopped the dam by three feet in 1890, leading to the four-foot difference at Wade's ranch.

dam was saved. The alarm had sounded, but most of those who had been involved with its design and construction simply hit the snooze button. No more warnings would occur; the next event would be the big one.

The only thing about which all writers agree is that the immediate cause of failure was an inadequate spillway. Engineer E. N. Robinson had designed a larger spillway remote from the dam (see page 52). Wells Bates was sufficiently concerned about the spillway to call in an outside expert, B. S. Church, for an opinion (see page 77 for quotes from Church's letter to Bates). Perhaps Bates was able to convince Van Beuren or Brodie that the spillway was inadequate because it was being enlarged at the time of failure (see the Brodie letter, page 133). The *location*—not just the size—of the spillway played a large factor in the failure, a fact that seemed to go unrecognized at the time and in subsequent accounts of the failure.

According to *Engineering News* (Mar. 8, 1890, p. 229) "... witnesses say that the water rushed through the [spillway] with terrible velocity, and kept 'increasing its width on the side next to the dam.'" Certainly that did not happen on the top of the dam as the man-made wall on the left side of the spillway is still intact as shown in Figure 5-10. Further along the spillway—downstream of the picture—the rock wall disappears and there is considerable erosion on the side toward the dam. Thus, it is possible that erosion of the spillway brought the discharge even closer to the toe of the dam and contributed to the failure by eroding the downstream face and the river bed, much as described by Brodie in his letter to Van Beuren (see page 134).

Figure 5-10. A view looking upstream along the spillway (Oct. 30, 2007). The rock wall on the right (left side of the spillway) is near the crest of the dam. The width is 31 feet measured from the rock wall to the natural rock on the other side. The original depth could not be determined due to debris.

In Appendix II I calculate the flow of the spillway—and of the spillway proposed by Robinson—and compare the numbers to the actual flood flow. I conclude that any proposed enlargement would have been insufficient to prevent overtopping and would not have saved the dam.

Blame

Men are only clever at shifting blame from their own shoulders to those of others. (Titus Livius, 59 BC 17 AD)

To err is human, to blame the next guy even more so. (Anon.)

There is a divergence of opinion as to the quality of the design and construction of Walnut Grove Dam. Everyone agrees that the immediate cause of the failure was an inadequate spillway. But had the size and placement of the spillway been satisfactory, was the dam doomed from the outset by bad design and bad construction, or would it have held for many years? That question raged in area and national newspapers and in engineering publications. What follows in this section is largely taken from the engineering literature with scant attention to newspaper accounts and editorials. I regard the latter as primarily uninformed in the technical details of the project except for what they have learned from the professionals who were involved; thus, it is much better to go directly to the professional literature.

The case against the dam

Wagoner (1888, p. 76) wrote critically about the dam *before* failure and thus his initial criticism is not part of the finger pointing that follows any disaster. Given Wagoner's qualifications (see page 54) and his subsequent history of excellent work, I take his comments seriously. Further, Wagoner's involvement with the actual design and construction appears to be minimal. Brodie (see page 132) wrote "...Mr. Luther Wagoner, C. E. was employed as Chief Engineer, but given solely charge of the survey for a flume line 19 miles in length from the dam to Fools Creek." In a letter dated March 24, 1890, to *Engineering News* (Apr. 5, 1890, p. 328) Wagoner wrote:

> After I took charge of the dam an assistant was detailed to inspect the work, and the terms of the contract were strictly complied with. Meantime, I was engaged in surveying a flume line, but I periodically

inspected progress of the work (at least once a week until its completion).

I reached Walnut Grove July 31, 1887 and took formal charge of the dam Aug. 10. During these ten days the work was practically left to the contractor to do as he pleased, and I was informed that it had been so the past month. During this time, the dam was raised about 20 ft. in height; this is the bad work mentioned in my account of the dam (see page 76, Proceedings of the Technical Society, Pac. Coast, 1888), where I say: "And the dam as originally built during a month's interval when there was no chief engineer some very bad work was done."

Thus, Wagoner had little to do with either the design or construction, his primary criticism came before failure, and he had little reason to point fingers at others. He wrote (Wagoner, 1888):

The history of the construction of the dam is one full of blunders, mainly caused by the officers of the company in New York. ... During the first stages of construction derricks were used to distribute the larger stones; later the center was kept high and the stones for the wall were moved by bars. The effect of this upon the stability of the dam is bad because it tends to form curved beds whose slope makes an acute angle with the direction of the resultant pressure. ... I advised the company to cut a large waste way and put the loose rock below the dam to strengthen this weak place. ... Labor was quite unreliable, perhaps owing to the presence of saloons and gambling shops, and the totally inadequate provision made for the comfort of the men by either the company or the contractor. This coupled with the intense heat, poor water and food, did not offer sufficient inducements to attract a sober and reliable class of workmen, a point too often over-looked in the construction of a large work.

Note that in his 1888 paper Wagoner advised a larger spillway (but, strangely, did not criticize its location). As far as I know he was the only one of the engineers who made the slightest attempt at determining flood flow in the Hassayampa (see page 18).

J. M. Currier, an engineer under Robinson, has expressed a mixed opinion in the *San Francisco Chronicle* (Feb. 26, p. 6). From the account of *Engineering News* (Mar. 8, p. 229):

... there was bad work in the bottom portion of the dam, and this was one of the reasons why Col. Robinson severed his connection with the dam and its owners. Mr. Currier ... claims that the foundation work was conducted very carefully, and not done in four feet of water as Mr. Wagoner stated; a coffer dam was sunk to bed rock in the rear of the wall, designed and commenced by Prof. Blake, and a solid wall, 18 ft. wide, was built up for the footing of the water face of the dam, and thus ignoring entirely the objectionable foot wall shown on the diagram presented by Mr. Wagoner. But Mr. Currier also says that it was impossible to exact good work from the men and material on hand and under the company's supervision; and that he was made to understand that "it was of more importance to float bonds and sell stock on Wall St., New York, than to construct a substantial dam." This engineer says he left the work in May, 1887, on account of the disgraceful manner in which it was then conducted, and that at that time the lower face of the dam was bulged. Heavy blasting was also done by the contractors, contrary to the engineer's positive orders, within 40 or 50 ft. of the foundation of the dam, and Mr. Currier believed "the whole foundation was shaken" by this blasting in the southeast corner of the dam.

James D. Schuyler was an eminent California engineer who had no direct involvement in the Walnut Grove Dam. He was materially involved with the design and construction of several dams in California, including rockfill dams. In his books (Schuyler, 1901, p. 58; Schuyler, 1909, p. 53) he wrote a scathing review of the Walnut Grove Dam, although much of it is taken from Wagoner (1888):

> Among the rock-fill dams that have ever been built or projected in the West unquestionably the slenderest and most flimsily constructed was that erected across the Hassayampa River, 30 miles south of Prescott, Arizona, in 1887-88, the destruction of which by a flood on the night[17] of February 22, 1890, was accompanied by the loss of 129[18] lives. This disastrous result was predicted when it was building by those familiar with its construction, as an event that was likely to occur, and the frightful consequences that ensued illustrate and emphasize the necessity and importance of governmental supervision of the plans and details of construction of all structures of that class, either by the State or Federal authorities. It should never have been permitted to

---

17. It was just after midnight the morning of February 22nd.

18. Schuyler could not have determined this number; the final death toll is unknown.

be built of the dimensions given to it, and the manner of its building was a conspicuous display of criminal neglect of all requisite precautions to secure the safety of any dam, and particularly one of the rock-fill type.

The dam was 110 feet high, 10 feet thick at the top, 138 feet thick at base, about 150 feet long at the bed of the stream, and 400 feet long on top. These dimensions would not have been excessive for an overall dam of solid masonry laid up in Portland cement, but for a rock-fill the slopes were so much steeper than the natural angle of repose of loose rock (20 horizontal to 47 vertical on the upper side, and 70 horizontal to 108 vertical on the lower side)[19] that it was really in danger of settling or sliding down to flatter slopes without the assistance of waterpressure against it. That it did not do so was solely due to the fact that the faces of the embankment were laid up as dry walls, each having a thickness of 14 feet at base and 4 feet at top, the center being a loose pile of random stone dumped in from a trestle. If these facing-walls had been carefully laid with large stones, on level beds, and an adequate spillway provided to carry the waste water around the dam and prevent it passing over the top, and if proper foundation had been laid for the entire structure, it might have been standing to-day.

Schuyler's case is damaged by a letter that he wrote to *Engineering News* (Sept. 22, 1888, p. 232) in which he defended rockfill dams in opposition to an editorial of a previous issue. In that letter he mentioned the "recently completed" Walnut Grove

---

19. The angle of repose for angular rock is a bit less than 45°, or a slope less than 1 to 1.

Dam and gave its dimensions with no criticism or prediction of failure. Even the myopic have 20-20 hindsight.

Engineering News weighed in with opinions after the failure. The editor's comments largely depended on statements of engineers involved in the design and construction and on newspaper articles. It went further, however, in blaming management, and in particular Van Beuren, for interfering with the engineering or not heeding engineering advice and for trying to build the project on the cheap. In the April 26, 1890, edition *Engineering News*, the editor opines (p. 399):

> When the truth is told it will be found that the dam was practically designed and constructed by laymen, and not by engineers at all; and that the disaster is the natural result of the foolish tinkering with a problem, the possibilities and dangers of which were not appreciated. In this case one man, and his family, practically furnished the large sum of money expended upon the dam and its outlying works, about $800,000[20] in all and by virtue of this moneyed control this man also assumed that he was competent to manage it as the engineer as well. With too many of his class, well-meaning but totally ignorant of the true dimensions of the problem involved, he thought that "any fellow" could be an engineer; and his willful neglect of the advice of his associates has cost him about one year's income out of an enormous estate, and has cost others all that they had—property and life. It is to be hoped that Mr. Van Buren [sic] has learned his lesson; and if he rebuilds the dam, as it is reported he will, that the work will be done throughout under competent engineering supervision.

---

20. About 18 million in 2007 dollars (cpi ratio = 22.9).

At this distance in time I am unable to evaluate the above statement. Certainly, the number of engineers in charge of the work was excessive and their tenure on the project short. That fact would indicate that a great deal of friction existed between the engineers and the management of the Walnut Grove Water Storage Company. E. N. Robinson had proposed a larger spillway at a remote location away from the dam and it is reasonable to make the conjecture that it was not built due to its cost. Van Beuren, however, was not one of the gold mining charlatans that mined not the land but investors pockets (an all-too-common practice with mining ventures; see, e.g., Burden and Stevens, 2006). He was active in the project, spent a large amount of time at the site and stayed with the ship after it hit the iceberg.

Although all agree the primary cause of the failure was an inadequate spillway it is remarkable that nowhere in the engineering literature or the newspaper accounts is mentioned the *placement* of the spillway at the end of the dam so that its flow entered the river adjacent to the toe. Probably overtopping of the dam would have been sufficient to cause failure, but had an adequate spillway been provided *in the same position* so that the dam would not be overtopped, the failure probably would have occurred due to erosion that undermined the dam. I cannot account for the fact that none of the engineers involved in the project recognized the importance of the spillway position.[21]

The case for the dam

It's difficult to defend failure, but some argue that the criticism about bad design and shoddy construction is negated by one

---

21. For anyone who might argue that the bedrock of the Hassayampa River could not be eroded, I invite them to read about the near loss of the left spillway of Glen Canyon Dam in 1983. In that case the water eroded through three feet of reinforced concrete then continued to carve a huge cavern in the rock abutment.

central fact: The dam withstood about six hours of overtopping up to a depth of three feet before failure[22,23] (*Engineering News*, Apr. 26, 1890, p. 390).

Indeed, I give that argument some validity; it is remarkable that Walnut Grove Dam did not fail hours before it did.

Wells Bates solicited the opinion of Benjamin S. Church, a well-known hydraulic engineer of the time, about the suitability of the spillway. Church visited the dam prior to its failure. He wrote in a letter dated March 27, 1890 (*Prescott Morning Courier*, Apr. 3, 1890; *Engineering News*, Apr. 26, 1890, p. 390):

> In answer to your inquiry as to my professional opinion regarding the cause of the destruction of the Walnut Grove Dam I have to say that in my judgment the disaster was evidently due to an underestimate of the volume of water which the waste weir, cut in rock at the end of the dam, would be called upon to pass during flood times.
>
> The dam itself was ample weight, and dimensions. The construction was sufficiently good, and the foundations solid. But the dam was intended to act only as

---

22. The rockfill Lake Avalon Dam on the Pecos River, New Mexico, failed by overtopping Aug. 3, 1893 (after completion in 1892) with less depth of water of water over the dam. Its spillway was rebuilt to 240 feet wide and depth of 15 feet below the crest of the dam. However, there was a subsequent failure in 1904 believed to be caused by leakage. The rebuilt dam had a concrete core wall (Schuyler, 1909, pp. 44–50).

23. Anon. (1936) states that water flowed "over the top [of the dam] four feet deep for 48 hours before it accomplished the collapse of the dam." Moritz (1945, p. 2) also reported that the dam was overtopped for 48 hours. He probably got this number from "narrative history," reproduced on page 100.

a reservoir embankment wall, built entirely of stone, over which it was designed that no water should ever pass.

The solidity of the structure of the dam itself is attested when you consider that it sustained a flow three feet in depth, over its crest for six hours before yielding to that extra-ordinary denuding dynamic force.

Its action under such abnormal conditions simply proved how well it could have sustained its legitimate static pressures.

Prior to my last visit to Arizona, you personally consulted me as a disinterested engineer not connected in any way with the work, about enlarging the waste weir.

When we visited the dam in December last, the work of enlarging its waste weir was in progress.

Although Church puts the entire blame on the inadequate spillway, his letter also takes aim at the owners:

The sad catastrophe overtaking the Walnut Grove Dam proves the importance (by no means generally realized by the public), of placing engineering works of such magnitude in the hands of experienced experts thoroughly competent to deal with all the hydraulic problems involved. ... it is to the interest of true economy of the part of companies, as well for the protection of outside interests, that engineering works of this nature should not alone be planned, but executed under the supervision and direct personal responsibility of some professional man of established ability.

Brodie in his report to Van Beuren (Appendix III) vigorously defends the dam against criticism in newspapers and the engineering literature. I believe that, indeed, Brodie has a valid point where he implies that much of the criticism comes from those who could not know the details of the construction. He says that the flood was of such an exceptional magnitude that it could not be predicted or designed against. I do think that the editor of *Engineering News* took some cheap shots at those involved, and in one case was forced to apologize.

Newspapers

The previous paragraphs outline the more-or-less technical aspects of the dam collapse. Some of the remarks of editors who, in spite of a profound lack of knowledge, feel that they must give an uninformed opinion on everything are listed below. In those days, editors' opinions were not set off on an editorial page but included in the informative articles. Here are a few samples, all to be evaluated in light of the above paragraphs.

- "Professor Blake, a Connecticut so-called engineer, was first elected to superintend the building [of the dam], and not giving satisfaction after one year or so dismissed ..." (*Arizona Daily Gazette*, Feb. 28, 1890).

- Blake's dam did not go to bedrock but rested on 12 feet of coarse sand and boulders (*Arizona Daily Gazette*, Feb. 28).

- "The contractors importuned Mr. Robinson to remove this dangerous structure [Blake's wall] and substitute a suitable one, but the engineer refused, saying it would be a useless cost of about $40,000, and thus it was allowed to remain undisturbed" (*Arizona Daily Gazette*, Feb. 28).

- "Waste way should have been at least 600 feet wide instead of 35" (*Arizona Daily Gazette*, Feb. 28).

- "Someone has been criminally careless in connection with this disaster and it will come to light someday." (*Arizona Daily Gazette*, Mar. 1).

- "This horrible disaster however may save still greater horrors in the future by teaching engineers and capital that nothing save a wide margin on absolute safety in dams will ever control water within this region of country." "Dam should have been 500 feet across" (*Phoenix Daily Herald*, Feb. 26). In the same issue Wagoner's statement that the "construction is full of blunders" (see page 55) was quoted—the first evidence that I have seen that the newspaper reporters or editors read any of the technical literature.

- The leak under the dam was 3000 miners inches (*Arizona Daily Gazette*, Feb. 25). [About 4800 cfs! Wagoner said that the dam leaked 141 inches (about 3.75 cfs) (*San Francisco Chronicle*, Feb. 24, 1890, p. 1].

The *San Francisco Chronicle* wrote scathing commentaries on the construction of the dam beginning on February 24, illustrating exactly what newspapers should not do. It starts by stating "[The failure was] caused by criminal carelessness in construction." Much of their article is based on an interview with Luther Wagoner, who was available in San Francisco. Wagoner cites his 1888 paper and said that he "warned the company of the dangerous condition of their dam." The most sensational part of the article was Wagoner's statement that "Robinson, the engineer in charge, who was a worthless drunkard, was shot gunned out of the place, and I met him a few days ago begging for money to get a meal with." The next day (Feb. 25):

> Luther Wagoner, when seen by the *Chronicle* yesterday, took issue with certain statements credited to him in an interview published in this paper, as to Colonel Robinson being a "worthless drunkard".

> "I have never met Mr. Robinson," said Mr. Wagoner, "and I know nothing whatsoever of his habits. The original designs of the dam were made by him, and I consider them good. ... The most probable cause of the failure, to my mind, is the notoriously bad work done after Colonel Robinson had left and up to the time of my taking hold."

In a letter he stated that the failure was due "to bad work done during the month or more between Colonel Robinson's retirement and my succession."

Lester Robinson's (Edwin's son) letter to the *San Francisco Chronicle* (Feb. 28, 1890, p. 3) states that the skin on the apron was not put down as per the original plans, "work on both the skin and tower was a disgrace" and the cause of breaking was due to poor work above the 40foot level (E. N. Robinson left when the dam had reached that height).

The Lower Dam

The Lower (diversion) dam did not materially affect the flood except, perhaps, locally. Most of the deaths took place at or near the lower dam, the deaths being blamed on Dan Burke for not warning those camped near the dam (see page 34). It was located 14.9 river miles (7.8 miles straight-line distance) from the main dam (see map in the Preface). Its purpose was the diversion of water—released from the main dam—from the river into a flume to the placer fields. Although the Lower dam was completed just before the flood, work was continuing on the flume. Since most of the ongoing work was in that vicinity, both Brodie and Van Beuren had their camps there.

The Lower dam was of rock-crib construction and stood 25 feet high. Its impediment to the flood waters was negligible and according to Brodie it "was entirely obliterated, not a vestige of it being left." Today only scant evidence of the site being occupied is apparent. Figure 5-11 shows a quarry on the right side of the river from which stone for the dam was apparently taken. On the left side of the river are several terraces used for roads or to make a semi-permanent camp (Figure 5-12). There is no evidence of the flume near the Lower dam site or immediately below it, but further downstream rock is blasted out of the right bank of the river to accommodate the flume line (Figure 5-13).

Figure 5-11. A quarry at the Lower dam site.

Figure 5-12. One of the terraces built for a road or camp.

Figure 5-13. Excavation for the flume from the Lower dam to the placer fields. This view is 2.8 miles downstream of the Lower dam and taken from the left bank of the river looking across the river.

Litigation

One can only imagine the financial consequences for actual losses, loss of life, pain and suffering, and punitive damages
that a dam failure today would generate considering the huge
amount of money that juries award for even minor injuries.
Eighteen-ninety, however, was another era. A lawsuit on the
Walnut Grove disaster was heard in February, 1891, in Maricopa County District Court with Judge Joseph H. Kibbey[24] pre-
siding. The case numbers, plaintiffs and amounts asked were[25]:

1083	Henry Wickenburg	$7888.00
1081	William Bacon	2853.50
1080	Lydia J. Conger	6350.00
1084	Edward Burr Wiggins	1355.00
1085	Josiah S. Bassett	4200.00
1087	W. S. Collier	436.20
1086	William H. South	2485.00
1088	G. A. Roberts	5490.00
1089	F. L. Brill	6000.00
1090	J. P. Evans	6050.00
1091	Henry Cowell	710.00
1092	Fred Hodder and W. S. Collier	464.00
1093	Fred Hodder	500.00
1082	Arthur S. Foushee (guardian)	50,000.00

24. Judge Kibbey became territorial governor in 1905 after Brodie resigned.

25. The plaintiff's names and the amounts come from three sources: the *Arizona Daily Gazette* of April 1, 1890, the *Prescott Journal Miner* of April 2, 1890, and court records (Arizona State Library and Archives, Phoenix). Some spelling and amounts may be incorrect due to legibility of the newspapers and of the court records. The total amount does not sum to that stated below

In total, 14 suits were filed. The largest claim was by A. S. Foushee, guardian, on behalf of Carrie Adelia Haynes (15 years old) and Ada Ella Haynes (18), two girls whose parents were killed. The total asked in the 14 cases was $93,000 (*Arizona Republican*, May 21, 1890), about 2.1 million in 2007 dollars[26].

The suits came before Judge Kibbey in May 1890, and a court date was set for December. Later that date was postponed until February 2, 1891. All of the cases were consolidated under that of Henry Wickenburg[27].

After a week of testimony, the jury was deadlocked. Judge Kibbey immediately impaneled another jury (Feb. 10) and the case began again. The second jury found in favor of the Walnut Grove Water Storage Company and Henry Van Beuren on Feb. 16. To add injury to injury, the plaintiffs were assessed the Company's costs in the following amounts: Lydia J. Conger, $10; William Bacon, $50; A. S. Foushee, $400; Edward B. Wiggins, $500; Josiah Bassett, $300; William H. South, $10; W. S. Collier, $80; G. A. Roberts, $10; F. L. Brill, $100; J. P. Evans, $10; Henry Cowell, $200; Frederick Hodder and W. S. Collier, $70; Frederick Hodder, $60. The Company withdrew its motion to recover costs from Henry Wickenburg.

Some of the court records are available on film and others in a bound (paper) volume at the Arizona State Archives in Phoenix.

---

26. To find the equivalent in 2007 dollars, multiply by 22.9.

27. Dill (1987, p. 302) reports that all of the suits were dismissed on grounds that they were filed in the wrong jurisdiction, in Maricopa County whereas the dam was located in Yavapai County. The court record shows that the jurisdiction argument was made emphatically by the attorneys for the Walnut Grove Water Storage Company. It does not contain the judge's decision, but the fact that the cases were tried in Maricopa County indicates that the jurisdiction argument was dismissed.

Unfortunately, these records are in bad order, some are repeated, and much is omitted. In addition to determining the outcome of the suits, the testimony would be extremely valuable in reconstructing the events, but neither the court testimony nor the answers to most of the interrogatories is in the record. The plaintiffs moved to set the adverse decision aside because it was contrary to the facts in the case but were unsuccessful.

The verdict is puzzling, especially in light of the inadequate spillway capacity and the general agreement at the time of that fact. In the case of the Johnstown flood the court was convinced that the dam collapse was due to a terrific flood that was "an act of God" and *could* not have been foreseen. In view of Brodie's statement (Appendix III, page 134) that the flood was "one of unprecedented ferocity ... and that within the memory of man there never had been so general and heavy a rain resulting in such terrible floods," the same argument may have been made in the case of the Walnut Grove Dam. The judge's instructions to the jury provided for such a case. In part they were[28]:

> And if by intelligent inquiry, taking into consideration all the sources of information, it could have been ascertained that an amount of water was occasionally, even if infrequently, discharged into the reservoir and against the dam, greater than the dam was designed and accordingly constructed to withstand, the omission to make such diligent inquiry is negligence, and if injury then be caused by the breaking of the dam because of such excessive amount of water, the defendant corporation would be liable therefore.

---

28. The judge's instructions were given in the case of Henry Wickenburg and are available on film at the Arizona State Libraries, Archives and Public Records.

But if you should believe from the evidence that defendant corporation made or caused to be made such diligent inquiry, and therefore constructed its dam so as to withstand the forces to which it might be subjected by ordinary recurring and expected floods, or those which after such inquiry might have been expected, and if such dam was destroyed by an extraordinary flood such as could not have been foreseen or anticipated or expected by the exercise of the diligent inquiry I have suggested, and the injury thereby caused of which the plaintiff complains, he cannot recover and you should find for the defendants.

Thus, the jury may have been persuaded that the flood that destroyed the dam was extraordinary and could not have been foreseen. But even if the jury did not believe that the flood was of an unprecedented magnitude, Judge Kibbey provided another escape route (And, yes, it is all one sentence):

If you should believe from the evidence that said Board caused plans, specifications and design for the creation of a reservoir at Walnut Grove, and the erection of a dam to impound the water therein, to be prepared by a person whom they reasonably believed to be a competent engineer, and that thereafter they on behalf of the corporation entered into a contract in good faith with persons whom they reasonably believed [illegible handwritten insertion] to be competent persons for the erection of said dam in accordance with such a plan, specifications and design, and such a dam and its appurtenances were accordingly constructed, or constructed according to such plan specifications and design modified by a person whom they reasonably [illegible handwritten insertion] believed to be competent to modify same, and that such construction was under the supervision of a person selected by said Board or its president whom in the exercise of reasonable care they reasonably believed to be competent therefore, then such president and members of such Board are not liable, even though you should believe from the evidence that there was a defect in the plans, specification or design prepared for such structure, or fault in the manner of construction, unless you further believe from the evidence that such president had actual notice of such defect or default, and that such president or Board of Directors had access to and may have seen such plans and specification, or may have seen the work progressing, or may have given directions in some part of its progress provided such directions were not contrary to such plans and specifications is not sufficient to charge him or them with knowledge of such defect if any there were if you believe that the preparation of such plans specifications and design required scientific knowledge and skill, and you do not believe from the evidence that such president of Board possessed such knowledge or skill, there is no presumption that any of them did.

Simply by turning the technical aspect over to a competent person, or a person that the Board of Directors and Van Beuren believed to be competent, they were relieved of liability. It would seem that Robinson must have been that competent person. But the fact that Robinson was fired in a bizarre manner only four months into the job and a non-engineer, Walter Bates, was appointed to supervise the job, and that Robinson's plans were not followed in that the spillway that he proposed was never built (see page 52), would appear to negate that argument. We will never know what the members of the jury were thinking.

CHAPTER 6:
HASSAYAMPA RIVER:1 890-2009

According to Judge Morrison, the 49ers gold rush in California has left a legacy that affects modern times (page 30). Mining in Arizona has also left environmental problems. The state has a large number of abandoned mines where, it seems, a life is lost every year when someone accidentally falls into a shaft or foolishly attempts to explore underground. Nearly all mines have tailings on the surface and these can leach heavy metals into the surface environment as well as provide sediment and can contaminate groundwater.

Due to the collapse of Walnut Grove Dam, the Hassayampa watershed escaped the sort of environmental destruction caused by hydraulic mining in California.[1] Did, however, the failure itself leave a long-lasting footprint? What was the effect of dam collapse and subsequent floods? How has the Hassayampa River fared in the last 119 years?

---

[1]. If you believe Corle (1951, p. 256), the flood brought an additional benefit. In a gratuitous statement laced with hyperbole he recounts the general lawlessness of the era and says "[The flood] purged the land of the greed and stench of man."

The dam failure caused documented, flood-induced, local changes through Wickenburg such as the destruction of arrastras and farmland[2] along the river and deposition of sand. According to Julia Macias

Brooks (current Executive Director of the Wickenburg Chamber of Commerce), whose family came to Wickenburg in 1857[3], the pre-1890 river was one-third to one-half of its current width and its banks

were lined with farmland, all of which was destroyed. In other stretches of the river major, long-lasting changes probably did not result from the dam collapse. Short duration, high intensity floods are not effective in causing large geomorphic changes in alluvial or bedrock channels because their total energy expenditures are low (Costa and O'Connor, 1995).

Webb, et al. (2007, p. 326) says that "The riparian ecosystem along the Hassayampa River is one of the most valued in western Arizona." Its most-visited area is the Hassayampa River Preserve—just southeast of Wickenburg in the 1890 location of Brill's farm—owned by The Nature Conservancy. The Hassayampa River Canyon Wilderness, which surrounds the site of the Lower dam and is managed by the United States Bureau of Land Management (BLM) (see map in Preface), is less developed and less well known but is a scenic spot for hikers.

---

2. According to local lore, Henry Wickenburg went into a deep depression after the loss of his farm. He never recovered and took his own life in 1905.

3. Note, however, that Conner (1956) did not mention that the Walker party encountered people other than Indians on their march up the Hassayampa in 1863.

Floods since 1890.

Floods on the Hassayampa can occur either due to intense summer thunderstorms or winter rainfall. Table 3[4] shows some of the high flows between 1890 and 2007, inclusive, through Box Canyon.

The flood of 1970

On September 3, 1970, tropical storm Norma pushed northward into Arizona where it collided with an intense cold front. Record rainfall occurred in Arizona, western New Mexico, southwest Colorado and southern Utah. That rain caused floods on the Hassayampa, Agua Fria and Verde rivers, among others, in central Arizona. The September 56 flood on the Hassayampa is the highest on record—remembering that the Walnut Grove Dam collapse occurred before any gaging stations were established—in Box Canyon. The flow reached 58,000 cfs. Flood marks in Box Canyon were 44 feet above the stream bed (Roeske, et al., 1978, pp. 28–29). Roeske says that the flood "is more than twice the previous maximum for the 50 years of record and is the largest flood since at least 1890 when the Walnut Grove Dam near Wagoner failed." Most of the flow was contributed by tributaries of the Hassayampa near the Walnut Grove Dam site.

No lives were lost along the Hassayampa[5], but damage was considerable in the vicinity of Wickenburg. The water reached a level of 16 feet near the Hassayampa River Preserve compared to the flow simulation of 28 feet in 1890. Roeske, et al.

---

4. See Durrenberger and Ingram (1978) for a list of floods in Arizona. The dates for Hassayampa floods in that book do not correlate well with those in the table.

5. See footnote 1 on page 1.

(1978, pp. 15–16) reports: "The flood deposited large amounts of sand in the channel [near Wickenburg] and on the low terraces. As much as 4 feet of sand and silt was deposited in the reach between 3 and 5 miles downstream from Wickenburg. Although the newly laid deposits were scoured during the waning stage of the flood, little erosion of the pre-flood deposits occurred."

Table 3. High flows at Box Canyon[a]

Year	Flow (cfs)	Return[b] years
1890	29,000c	20
1891	unknown	-----
1911	unknown	-----
1916	unknown	-----
1925	25,500	17
1927	27,100	18
1937	22,000	14
1951	27,000	18
1970	58,000	74
1991	13,700d	8
1993	25,748	17
1995	13,016	7
2005	19,094	11

a. Data from the U. S. Geological Survey and the Flood Control District of Maricopa County
b. Flood frequency has been calculated by FCDMC for 2, 5, 10, 20, 50 and 100 years. The numbers shown in this column result from linear interpolation.
c. A gross estimate for the flow and return period that would have occurred in Box Canyon in the absence of the dam (see the section on River Flow, page 121).
d. At Morristown.

This flood is the nearest that compares with that of the dam failure and the effects on the river were probably similar. In 1890 considerable erosion probably occurred in the initial stages, when the flood wave hit. The erosion was followed by aggra-dation, especially on the terraces near the river where plant life would slow the flow and cause deposition. Then at least some of the sand that was deposited on the terraces would be washed back into the river when the water level dropped. The result would be extensive damage or destruction to agricul-tural lands—initially carrying away topsoil and then replacing it with sand—and destruction of much of the riparian plants along the river. A number of papers and books (e.g., Webb, et al., 2007) describe in detail the effect on the riparian plant life[6] following floods of various magnitudes.

Extreme floods

The estimate of the 1890 flow that would have occurred had the Walnut Grove Dam not been built (see the section on River Flow, page 121), although the second largest in Table 3, is only 27% of the 1970 flood. Although no records exist, accounts of the flood of 1891 indicate that it was larger than the 1890 flow (in the absence of the dam). There have been studies of large and medium magnitude floods on rivers and streams in the South-west and throughout the world (see, e.g., Kochel, 1988 and Ely, 1997). The Plum Creek flood of 1965 near Denver had a return period between 900 and 1600 years and was 15 times larger than the 50-year flood for that stream (Osterkamp and Costa, 1987).

---

6. Riparian plants occur along intermittent streams but not along ephemeral streams (see footnote page 12). The plants along ephemeral streams are the same as those in the surroundings. The brighter green riparian plants such as cottonwoods and willows are a consequence of the constant supply of water along intermittent streams.

The fact that such catastrophic floods can and do occur empha-sizes the need to design dams and other critical infrastructure to withstand them.

The Plum Creek channel was widened considerably and most vegetation was destroyed. Normally vegetation on the banks and terraces has a protective effect against erosion, but in extremes this vegetation is lost, leading to undercutting of banks and widening of the primary channel. In the case of Plum Creek, a large amount of coarse sediment was deposited in the main channel and the sinuosity of the channel *was* great-ly *decreased.* How this applies to *the* 1890 Hassayampa flood is uncertain because in the Plum Creek case much of the sediment came from the tributaries whereas the Hassayampa tributaries did not suffer extreme flooding, although they were definitely in a flood situation. Also, much of the Hassayampa is confined to a canyon, the walls of which are not as subject to erosion as the floodplains of most rivers and thus the sinuosity could not have changed drastically. However, the impoundment behind the dam must have accumulated sediment that was then carried down the river.

Other floods

If the Walnut Grove Dam had survived the 1890 flood, it would have been severely tested almost exactly one year later. The *Arizona Republic* of February 18, 1891, with dateline Prescott, states:

> The heaviest storm ever known here has been raging since Monday morning, excelling the noted one a year ago, when the Walnut Grove Dam washed away. At 8 p. m. Granite Creek is a foot to a foot and a half high-er than during the storm of last February, and is rising

rapidly ... fears are entertained that the disaster of a year ago may be repeated by the washing out of the dam on Lynx Creek (see page 21).

The fears were well founded; the Lynx Creek Dam did collapse. Pictures of the failed structure appear in Schuyler (1909, p. 291).

Table 3 shows that the Hassayampa has had a series of floods since 1890, all but one less than a 20-year return period or of an unknown return period. Such floods can do considerable damage to the infrastructure (Figure 6-1). However, they are part of a natural process for Southwestern rivers and creeks. The riparian forests along rivers depend on periodic floods for seed dispersal, for the establishment of terraces and floodplains, and to clear out small vegetation. Changes in

riparian vegetation occur when a river is dammed, thus preventing flooding (Stromberg, et al, 1993, p. 118)[7].

Stromberg, et al. (1993) and Stromberg, et al. (1997) have studied the effect of the 1991, 1993 and 1995 floods on the Hassayampa in the vicinity of the Hassayampa River Preserve. In 1991 the floodplains were aggraded; in the larger flood of 1993 the terraces were eroded and the main channel was widened from about 10 feet to about 160 feet. In 1995 there was again deposition.

---

7. The disappearance of sand beaches and consequential effect on plant and fish life in the Grand Canyon led the U.S. Department of the Interior to release high flows or artificial floods from Glen Canyon Dam in 1996, 2004 and 2008. One objective was to deposit sand that had originated in tributaries below Glen Canyon Dam onto beaches in the canyon, thus creating favorable habitat for native fish. Some beaches were successfully enhanced, but their longevity was compromised by routine dam operation. The overall value of the artificial floods—especially compared to their cost, mostly loss of hydroelectric power—remains a matter of opinion.

Figure 6-1. The flood of 1916 destroyed the bridge across the river at Wickenburg.

Although human activities (overgrazing, groundwater pump-ing, agriculture, urban development, highways and bridges) have had considerable effect on rivers and streams, probably none is as important as dam construction. These activities have changed the Hassayampa, but as one of the last free-flowing riv-ers in Arizona it has still not suffered the fate of the Salt, Gila and other rivers. The legacy of the Walnut Grove Dam failure is uncertain. Most of the effects were probably nullified by the 1970 flood and since that time nature has taken its course in periodic flooding and drought.

CHAPTER 7: REBUILDING

The failure proved that the flow in the Hassayampa River was sufficient to fill the reservoir. The gold fields still remained to be exploited. Hydroelectric power was becoming popular. Irrigation in the arid west was proving its worth. A new dam could be bigger and better—and multipurpose. There was every reason to rebuild the dam; the primary obstacle was financing the project.

Rebuilding Walnut Grove Dam

Efforts to rebuild the dam began shortly after the collapse. The *Phoenix Daily Herald* (Mar. 6, 1890) reported that "Already preliminaries are being arranged for the reconstruction of the Walnut Grove Dam and for the building of yet another large reservoir in that region." From the *Coconino Sun*, Jan. 7, 1892, "Supt. Brodie ready to rebuild Walnut dam site." The *Arizona Daily Journal-Minor* of Nov. 22, 1902, reported "John Haulon [sic] is in town from Walnut Grove, where he is superintending the annual assessment work on the dam of the Walnut Grove Water Storage Company. What a magnificent enterprise this water storage will be when it is again realized." A newspaper reported that "Mrs. Eleanor C. Wittmann [Eleanor Van Beuren Wittmann,

Henry Van Beuren's daughter[1]], a millionaire woman of Philadelphia, is preparing to fulfill the promise she made to her father on his dying bed and rebuild the Walnut Grove Dam, proving that it can be made an instrument for happiness instead of human destruction." (Henry Van Beuren died Nov. 29, 1906.) A brochure from Wall Street, New York, dated Aug. 9, 1892, represented an attempt to sell stock or otherwise arrange financing. It states:

> Since the reservoir and service dams were carried out by the flood ..., the company has employed hydraulic engineers and miners of high standing and of practical experience in their business to personally investigate the property of the company to determine whether it was feasible to rebuild the dams with certain modifications suggested by experience in construction, and to test the gravel on the company's mining claims. These examinations have been thorough and long continued, and they have been conducted under the personal direction of the President of the company. They have resulted in the emphatic conclusions that the scheme is entirely practicable, and that the returns reasonably to be expected fully warrant the required outlay.
>
> The area of land which can be irrigated by the company's water supply is very large; without water this land is valueless for agricultural purposes, but with water, it will produce sub-tropical fruits and cereals

---

1. Eleanor was camped with Henry Van Beuren and Mary Hanlon, but at the time of collapse was in Phoenix with Henry.

in very profitable abundance and of excellent quality. With the water, the placer mines can be operated successfully and profitably but without it they are of little or no value.

These efforts were thwarted by the continuing legal difficulties of the Walnut Grove Water Storage Company. P. M. and Jackson Mognett brought suit (1) to restore their original land (in the Minnehaha area, east of the dam site, where timber was harvested) occupied by the Company, (2) to be paid restitution of $6000 and (3) to be paid $4000 for rents, profits and cost of 15,000 feet of lumber[2]. The court ruled against the plaintiff on all counts and assessed them the defendant's costs of the trial. Another suit by William E. Wicks also ended in a decision for the Company.

The above must have been considered nuisances by the Company, but the suit[3] brought by the Farmers Loan and Trust Company was a killer. It was filed Oct. 17, 1891, and lasted until June 1908, preventing the Company, Van Beuren and his daughter, Eleanor, from taking financial action to rebuild the dam. The suit sought foreclosure of a $350,000 loan that went into default on June 1, 1890. The loan was secured by 63 placer mining claims in the Weaver Mining District. In the initial court case, the plaintiff asked that a receiver be appointed, which was granted when the Company did not appear in court. Alexander O. Brodie was appointed receiver on October 31, 1891, a position that he held until February 9, 1905, just before his resignation as governor of Arizona on February 14. At that time John Hanlon, Brodie's brother-in-law, took the position.

---

2. Case 1484 in the District Court of Yavapai County.

3. Case 1973 in the District Court of Yavapai County.

Henry Van Beuren had "bought and paid for the receivers certificates up to the time of his death in order to keep said property intact and with a view of erecting a new Dam on the site of the old one, with such modifications as appeared to be necessary in order to avoid a re-occurrence of such a disaster, but no capital for such an enterprise has ever been raised ..."[4] Van Beuren had to pay to maintain the property and the mining claims, the latter costing $3000 per year, or the property would revert to the U.S. government. The receiver's expenses and salary were paid by Van Beuren.

Upon Van Beuren's death (Nov. 29, 1906), Eleanor was appointed administrator of his estate. In March, 1908, Eleanor petitioned the Yavapai District Court that the property should be sold, ostensibly to relieve her of the expenses, but her real reason was that she wanted to buy the property, end the court proceedings and get on with rebuilding the dam. The property was sold at auction in June, 1908, Eleanor being the only bidder. All of the Company's assets were transferred to her by a Master Commissioner's Deed (Moritz, 1948, legal notice in the *Prescott Morning Courier*, May 9 and May 11, 1908, p. 4).

Box Canyon Dam, the Nadaburg Project

Somewhere along the line the idea of building a dam at the original site was abandoned, or, perhaps, a series of dams was contemplated. Without a dam at the original site, the goal of hydraulic mining was not feasible, so the purpose of a storage

---

4. Case 1973 in the District Court of Yavapai County.

reservoir became irrigation. A very favorable location for a dam was in Box Canyon, about eight miles north of Wickenburg (see map in Preface; see Figure 7-1). In 1910 Mrs. Wittmann hired engineers to investigate the feasibility of power and irrigation using the Hassayampa River and made applications for rights-of-way for a reservoir and dam site in Box Canyon as well as for a canal along the river over government land. Mrs. Wittmann's engineers established a gaging station in Box Canyon, surveyed the area and generally investigated the practicability of the project.

Figure 7-1. The Hassayampa River in "The Narrows" of Box Canyon.

The Carey Act

The Carey Act was signed into law on August 18, 1894. It was intended to promote irrigation on arid lands in the western United States. Up to one million acres of land in each state could be transferred from the federal government to the state and, ultimately, to private ownership. The provisions of the act took effect in each state at different times; in Arizona it became effective on January 1, 1914. On that same day Mrs. Wittmann filed an application for 17,600 acres in the Morristown area. The application was granted on April 14, 1916 (Moritz, 1945).

After Eleanor's death in 1917, Joseph Wittmann continued the effort to construct a dam. He[5] filed an application with the State Water Commission in January 1922, for a use permit for water from the Hassayampa. The Nadaburg Irrigation District, named for the town of Nadaburg[6]—to become the Arizona Water Conservation District in 1929—was created in June 1923, by a group of homesteaders. That District is shown on the location map, Figure 7-2. The permit to irrigate 25,000 acres was issued on March 5, 1924. Three-fourths of the land in the Nadaburg Irrigation District was deeded to Joseph Wittmann by the landowners by an agreement made in 1928. In return Wittmann transferred water rights from Carey Act lands to District lands so

---

5. Moritz (1945) states that the application was filed by Eleanor, which is hardly possible considering her death in 1917.

6. The name is a whimsical combination of the Spanish "nada," meaning "nothing," and the English use of "burg," meaning a small town. The name was changed to Wittmann in 1929 "... for [the] man who financed rebuilding of Walnut Grove Dam and irrigation plant" (Barnes, 1988). When the irrigation plan was abandoned, there was a move to change the name back to Nadaburg, but it has remained Wittmann. The former name lives on in the Nadaburg School District and Nadaburg Elementary School.

that he could proceed on the construction of the entire project. The United States General Land Office approved the transfer on May 19, 1928 (Moritz, 1945).

Financing

The above legal maneuvering paved the way for the realization of the project; only the small detail of financing remained. On April 24, 1933, the Arizona Water Conservation District filed for a loan of $1,925,000 with the Reconstruction Finance Corporation (an agency of the U. S. Government created by President Hoover in 1932). The stock market crash had occurred on October 24, 1929 ("Black Tuesday"), and by 1932 the country was mired in the "Great Depression." The application was later transferred the Public Works Administration[7]. According to Moritz (1945, p. 3):

> A supplemental application was filed with the Public Works Administration in November 1933, to conform with the requirements of the National [Industrial] Recovery Act [enacted June 16, 1933, to promote employment], and changed the amount of the requested loan and grant to $2,350,000. The state engineers for the Public Works Administration would not approve the grant, one of the reasons being that the project appeared to be largely a land promotion scheme for one interest.

---

7. The PWA was a depression-era, New Deal agency formed, primarily, to provide employment in that bleak time. It was used to build Grand Coulee and Bonneville dams among many other projects.

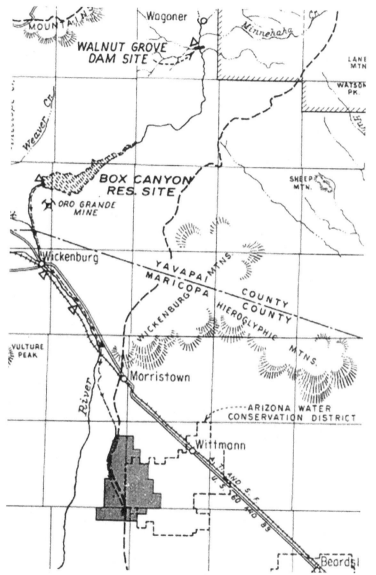

Figure 7-2. Location map (Moritz, 1945). The Nadaburg Irrigation District (renamed Arizona Water Conservation District) is within the dashed lines. The dark area represents the area that was to be irrigated from the Box Canyon Dam. Although the District area and the project area overlap, they are not coincident. The heavy dashed line is the boundary of the Hassayampa River drainage area.

The district filed an amendment to their application to the Public Works Administration in September 1936, changing their plans somewhat and advising the Public Works Administration that Wittmann would deed the district 7500 acres of land to be sold to help retire the bonds to be issued. The total cost of the project under the amended application was estimated at $1,851,000. The Public Works Administration approved the amended application, but no allotment was made out of the 1938 appropriation. The district made application to the Reconstruction Finance Corporation in October 1938, for a loan of $2,000,000 to construct the irrigation works as set forth in their application to the Public Works Administration, but the executive committee of the Reconstruction Finance Corporation refused the application for the loan.

Prospects

The Wittmanns had hired William A. Farish as the chief engineer on the project. If anyone could make it a success, Farish seemed to be the right person in the right place. He was the first city manager in Phoenix, he surveyed the Apache Trail (the road leading from Phoenix up the Salt River to Roosevelt Dam), and he laid out much of the early irrigation system in the Phoenix vicinity. His death in 1936 must have been a blow to the Wittmann project (obituary in the *Wickenburg Sun*, May 1, 1936 and the *Arizona Republic*, May 1, 1936).

Nevertheless, the prospect for the Wittmann project looked good, according to the press. Sam Smith, president of the Arizona Water Conservation District, promised to redouble efforts to carry the project forward. He said: "The building of a dam in the Box Canyon of the Hassayampa river would result in the formation of a lake 13 miles long, which would add immensely to the recreational attraction of Wickenburg. In addition to this the establishment of a highly productive farming area 14 miles south of Wickenburg and directly in town's trade area would be a powerful stimulus to Wickenburg business" (*Wickenburg Sun*, May 1, 1936). That same issue of the *Sun* published a letter to Smith from Wittmann in which Wittmann complained of a rumor that there was $1,000,000 in a trust fund for the construction of the project and, if so, that outside sponsorship was unnecessary. To refute that rumor, Wittmann enclosed a "narrative history of the Hassayampa river project," which the *Sun* published "in full":

> For many years following the close of the Civil war the U. S. army was extensively employed in quelling Indian disturbances in the thinly settled part of the country. The reconnaissances of the soldiers led them into unexplored areas, and many mines and ore deposits were discovered in this manner. The Arizona placer gold deposits in the Bill Williams region, in the Weaver district and on the Hassayampa river were doubtless among those so found.
>
> In 1883 two brothers, Charles [sic] and DeWitt C. Bates, located and filed on certain placer claims on the Hassayampa river, and seem to have been able to interest capital sufficiently to bring about on May 5, 1886, the incorporation of the Walnut Grove Water Storage company for the purpose of rescuing gold from the placer claims of the Bates brothers. A bond

issue was effected through the Farmers Loan and Trust company of New York which sold a large number of the bonds to Mrs. Mary S. Van Beuren of New York and to her son, Henry S. Van Beuren.

For the purpose of checking up on these investments, aggregating approximately $1,000,000, Mr. Henry S. Van Beuren, having been elected a director on June 4, 1886, visited the project where the Walnut Grove Dam was in process of construction at Wagoner, Ariz., on December 8, 1886. Mr. Van Beuren was elected treasurer, and on June 12, 1888, he became president.

The dam was completed in this year, and the flume line construction was begun to convey the water about 20 miles to the placers. The reservoir gradually filled up and for nearly two years the lake gave pleasure to many who sailed and rowed their boats on it. This source of pleasure was destroyed when, on February 22, 1890, the dam, which was not constructed as an overflow type, was carried away by a flood which swelled the river beyond the capacity of the spillway, flowing over the top four feet deep for 48 hours [see footnote on page 77 and the material referenced by the footnote] before it accomplished the collapse of the dam.

As a result of the catastrophe which overtook the project, a receiver was appointed. In 1891 the company also issued a note for $350,000 to Mr. Van Beuren covering cash theretofore furnished in addition to stock and bond investments made by him.

In order to keep intact the water rights of the company, Mr. Van Beuren paid all expenses of the receivership and the assessment work on the placer claims as required by law until his death on November 29, 1906.

At some point in this process the son of Joseph and Eleanor Van Beuren Wittmann, Joseph Van Beuren Wittmann, apparently took a major role in the project. The *Wickenburg Sun* (Nov. 6, 1936) reports his visit as owner of the Arizona Water Conservation District stating that "he was frank in declaring that the prospects for a successful issue of the enterprise were very promising at this time."

According to the *Wickenburg Sun* (July 8, 1937) the prospect brightened considerably when the Public Works Administration made conditional approval of a $2,000,000 application, which consisted of a $900,000 grant and a $1,100,000 loan. All that remained, according to the *Sun*, was proof of ownership of 7500 acres of tax-paid land, a satisfactory colonization program, and approval by President Roosevelt and Harold L. Ickes (PWA administrator) to make the project eligible for an allocation. A Phoenix PWA official said that the project should have little difficulty in meeting these conditions as the project has passed through the legal, engineering and financial examining divisions. The *Sun* article states that the "impounding Structure would be known as the 'Van Buren [sic] dam.'" and goes on to describe it in some detail.

Joseph Van Beuren Wittmann, "principal of the Arizona Water Conservation District," appeared before the Roundup Club (Wickenburg Chamber of Commerce) stating that the application had been approved by the Public Works Administration and "awaits only allocation of funds" (*Wickenburg Sun*, Sept. 17,

1937). Club members voted to endorse the project as a flood control measure.

A Roundup Club meeting was held in Phoenix in which Howard S. Reed, state PWA engineer, gave assurance of support, as did C. Warren Peterson, a member of the Maricopa Board of Supervisors (*Wickenburg Sun*, Oct. 8, 1937; see also the *Arizona Republic*, Oct. 7, 1937) where "sentiment was unanimously in behalf of the project and there were no objectors. Howard S. Reed spoke in behalf of the projects[8] and assurance of the county's support and co-operation if they are undertaken was given by George Frye, member of the board of supervisors. Warren Peterson, board chairman, also spoke in support of the Box Canyon dam project." Then: "The examining board made no commitment as to what recommendations it will make on the proposed project, nor is one expected immediately, as it will make a detailed study of the transcript of proceedings and documents pertaining to the project that were filed, before submitting final documents."

A negative indication came on August 19, 1938 (*The Arizona Republic*) when Arizona Senator Carl Hayden was advised that the project had been "deferred," and that a revision of the project would be necessary before any further action would be taken. Stephen W. Langmade, attorney for the Wittmann Irrigation District, said the objection was based on the fact that 7000 acres of the 19,000-acre tract were owned by Joseph Wittmann. He also stated that no immediate plans were being considered for a revision of the PWA project.

---

8. The plural is used here because the meeting also concerned a flood control project at Queen Creek.

The Roundup Club in a meeting July 9, 1941, upon hearing a rumor that there was still a possibility of building the project, appointed a committee to investigate. An examination of the minutes of the Club did not show that the committee made a report. On December 7 of that year the U.S. entered World War II and thoughts of the project were put on hold for the duration of the war.

Reports

Moritz (1948, p. 34) lists the reports on the Box Canyon project. They are: "Report on the Maricopa County Irrigation District Number 1" (the Arizona Water Conservation District), J. G. White Engineering Corporation, New York, 1927; a report by J. A. Fraps to W. W. Lane, State Engineer, State of Arizona, on hydroelectric potential of the Hassayampa River; and "Field Report on Application of Arizona Water Conservation District, Docket No. 551" by the Chief Engineer, Engineering Division, State of Arizona, 1937. In addition there are references to reports by W. A. Farish to the PWA, W. C. Lefeber to the Arizona Water Conservation District and A. S. Crane to the Arizona Water Conservation District.

The Fraps report concluded that hydroelectric production was not feasible. Moritz considers the "Field Report ..." as the most comprehensive. It estimated the cost of the entire system as $2,000,000 to irrigate 14,450 acres net or 18,062 acres gross[9]. A grant from the Public Works Administration was to provide 45%. J. W. Wittmann would donate 7000 acres, the proceeds of which would service the bond debt.

---

9. I don't know how these figures were calculated.

The USBR report

In 1945 the project was still alive, at least until the U.S. Bureau of Reclamation[10] made its preliminary report (Moritz, 1945). The final USBR report (Moritz, 1948) is everything that should have been done for the Walnut Grove Dam but wasn't. Of course, in the 1940s, there were much more data and Moritz had the advantage of a half-century of engineering advances and hindsight, but, most importantly, government agencies that were to supply funds required a comprehensive analysis. The study included the suitability of lands for irrigated farming, crop yields, water requirements for irrigation, hydrographic analysis of the Hassayampa River (including a flow-frequency curve and determination of the maximum probable flood), assessment of the dam site in Box Canyon, alternatives to the dam and irrigation project, the design of the dam, the design of a conduit and canals[11], and an economic analysis. Some items in the report follow.

The Box Canyon Dam. The dam[12] was to be 246 feet high and would store a maximum of 190,000 acre-feet of water. The reservoir

---

10. The Boulder Canyon Act authorized the Department of the Interior to investigate the feasibility of water projects in states that bordered the Colorado River and its tributaries.

11. The *Wickenburg Sun* (July 8, 1937) reported that a sheetpile diversion dam was to be constructed at about the point that the railroad crosses the Hassayampa eight miles southeast of Wickenburg. Moritz made no mention of such a structure and it would not be needed given the closed conduit that would carry water from the dam site.

12. The dam was to be rockfill and earth construction, according to Moritz, even though the narrows seems to be a good site for a masonry arch dam (see Figure 7-1). The *Wickenburg Sun* of July 8, 1937, reported that the dam would be an arch dam, which might imply that it would be of masonry construction. The plans called for a dam 1120 feet long curved in a 750-foot radius downstream of the narrows.

would consist of 10,000 acre-feet dead storage reserved for silt, 70,000 acre-feet of primary water supply, 120,000 acre-feet of secondary water supply and 10,000 acre-feet for flood control.

Spillway. The capacity was to be 69,700 cfs and it was to be located across a ridge some 4000 feet north of the dam. The spillway flow would be returned to the river almost a mile downstream of the dam—a very different situation than was constructed at the Walnut Grove site.

Outlet. The outlet works would have a capacity of 500 cfs. Water for the irrigation scheme would be carried in a circular concrete pipe buried in the sand of the river and have a capacity of 110 cfs.

Irrigation. From the end of the outlet pipe, water would be carried in an open, clay-lined canal to the irrigation area. The irrigation system would be composed of 75 miles of canals to irrigate 10,000 acres[13]. The main canal would consist of four tunnels having a combined length of 9130 feet.

Power. The report concluded that power generation would not be economical, even if the basic structure existed for other purposes so that power revenue would not have to pay a portion of the capital cost of the dam.

Flood control. Flood control was needed to protect Wickenburg, the highway between Wickenburg and Morristown, the railroad along the river, and irrigated land and irrigation structures near the Gila River. Flood damages were estimated to be $14,400 annually, which would be reduced by $11,900.

---

13. Some newspaper accounts give up to 20,000 acres (e.g., the *Wickenburg Sun* of July 8, 1937). The figure for total length of the canals (75 miles) also comes from the *Sun*; thus, the actual length in the final design is probably much less.

Domestic water supply. The reservoir could supply water to Wickenburg and to some of the farms in the vicinity.

Recreation. The preliminary report (Moritz, 1945) dismisses entirely use of the reservoir for recreation. The reasons are that the water would be used for domestic supplies—thus swimming, boating and fishing would be prohibited, and picnicking discouraged—and extreme variations in water level might create an uncomfortable or dangerous situation[14]. The final report (Moritz, 1948) states that the National Park Service estimated annual recreational benefits of $28,200 with an operational cost of $13,000.

Fish and wildlife. The Fish and Wildlife Service estimated an annual benefit of $18,000.

Economic analysis

Moritz (1948, p. 5) presents the following summary of costs and benefits[15]. The estimated costs were:

Investigations and surveys	$80,000
Box Canyon dam and reservoir	7,500,000
Main Canal	4,700,000
Lateral system	180,000
O & M during construction	70,000
Municipal and farmstead water system	370,000
Subtotal	$12,900,000
Recreation facilities	179,000
Total	$13,079,000

14. Recreation had been touted as a major asset for the project (*Wickenburg Sun*, May 1, 1936).
15. The cpi ratio 1948/2007 is 8.67 (i.e., multiply the following dollar figures by 8.67 to obtain equivalent 2007 dollars).

Direct annual benefits were estimated as (Moritz, 1948, p. 28):

Irrigation (10,000 ac) and farmstead water	$826,600
Municipal and domestic water supply	14,600
Flood control	11,900
Recreation	28,200
Fish and wildlife conservation	18,000
Total annual benefit	$899,300

The annual costs were (Moritz, 1948, p. 28):

O & M irrigation and farmstead water	$35,400
O & M municipal water	7,400
O & M recreation	13,800
Total operation and maintenance	$56,600
Amortization of construction costs	508,400
Total annual cost	$565,000

These figures give a benefit/cost ration of 1.59. Moritz (1948, p. 43-44) lists indirect benefits[16]:

(a) The addition of 10,000 acres of high value to the tax base and increased income taxes from that land.
(b) An increase of about three-quarter million dollars annually to Maricopa County. The result would be an increase "for domestic and professional services; for common labor; for transportation and utilities; for processing and packing facilities; for the goods and services required by approximately 130 families

---

16. The USBR has come under much criticism from economists for counting indirect benefits to justify projects. Much of the so-called indirect benefits constitute double counting. Since no dollar value is given in this case, the indirect benefits do not matter.

who will participate directly in farming; and for an appreciably greater number of families who will provide services for the people."

(c) Reconversion from a war to a peace economy with the opportunity for employment of war veterans and those displaced from war manufacturing.

Although the benefit/cost ratio was favorable, the major stumbling block was in the beneficiaries' ability to pay for the project. Moritz (1948, p. 24) puts the maximum repayment for irrigation and farmstead water at $2,940,000 plus that for municipal water at $185,000 totaling $3,125,000 or $73,500 per year over a 40-year repayment period. The repayment would amount to 27% of the costs over 40 years, or the repayment would require 150 years.

The dismal forecast for repayment apparently doomed the project. Moritz' final recommendations were:

(1) Construction of the Hassayampa Project for irrigation, flood control, domestic and municipal water supply, recreation, and fish and wildlife propagation be not authorized at this time.

(2) Further consideration of authorization be deferred until such time as the economic need of the Nation, lower construction costs, further information on the project, or other developments may justify such reconsideration; and

(3) The operation of the gaging stations at Box Canyon and Morristown be continued by the Geological Survey.

Box Canyon Dam, FCDMC

In 1963 the Flood Control District of Maricopa County[17]—established August 3, 1959—issued a report concerning projects in all of Maricopa County. Although Box Canyon is in Yavapai County, it is close to the county line and any project built there would have nearly all of its effect in Maricopa County.

The FCDMC did no analysis on their own but depended on the USBR report. They list a cost of $7,600,000[18], which did not include any of the irrigation works[19]. They list $290,000 in annual benefits, which consist of $20,000 for flood control, $262,000 for domestic water supply and $8000 in recreation benefits. The benefit-cost ratio was given as 0.90. Projects were listed in two categories: "recommended" and "not recommended." The Box Canyon dam made the not recommended list.

The FCDMC considered several other projects on tributaries to the Hassayampa in the Wickenburg area. These were Matthie Dam on Sols Wash, eight miles west of Wickenburg, where the major benefit would come from recreation (not recommended); Flying E Wash dam, west of Wickenburg (not recommended);

---

17. Maricopa County has an area of 9224 square miles. If it were a state, it would rank ahead of New Jersey, Connecticut, Delaware, and Rhode Island in area.

18. There seems to be a discrepancy of $100,000 from the table on page 105.

19. The FCDMC says that "This [project] has been abandoned due to insufficient water for irrigation" whereas Moritz (1948) seems to indicate that it was not recommended because of unfavorable financial considerations. The two are linked in that more water would enable a larger project that might have resulted in more favorable finances.

Casandro Wash Dam, in the west part of Wickenburg (recommended and built about 1996), Powder House Wash Dam,
northeast of Wickenburg (recommended but not constructed),
plus some channel improvements.

Box Canyon Dam, Wickenburg efforts

The USBR reports put to rest the Nadaburg irrigation project,
but the idea of a dam in Box Canyon was not quite dead. The
Wickenburg Town Council held a special meeting on May
23, 1968, to discuss the possibility of dam in Box Canyon for
recreational purposes. Although flood control was mentioned,
that seemed to be a secondary consideration. At that meeting
the Council voted to hire the engineering consulting firm W. S.
Gookin and Associates to conduct a preliminary study for a cost
of $2500.

The Gookin Report

Gookin and Associates issued their report on August 23, 1968. It
is published in full in the *Wickenburg Sun* of October 3, 1968.

Gookin initially considered the Bureau of Reclamation dam site
but dismissed it because of the cost. The site did not lend itself
to a smaller and less expensive dam because the dam needed to
be 246 feet high to accommodate a spillway across a saddle to
the northeast. Also, any size of dam would require excavation
to bedrock, approximately 100 feet below stream level. Instead,
Gookin proposed constructing the dam in the Narrows of Box
Canyon (Figure 7-1), approximately 3000 feet upstream of the
USBR site. Instead of excavating to bedrock they would build a
long concrete apron so that the seepage distance under the dam

would be long enough to preclude piping[20]. The spillway would be of the "ski-jump" type[21] with the overflow entering the river

600 feet downstream of the toe of the dam. The dam was to be 100 feet high, which would create a lake with 20,000 acre-feet volume and a surface area of 590 acres.

The Gookin report does not mention flood control. They estimated that the river flow would be sufficient "in all but the driest years" to replace water lost to evaporation and, thus, maintain a constant water level, which would enhance the recreational aspects. Reservoir operation for flood control requires that a reservoir be drawn down to provide storage to attenuate the peak flows. The report adds the seepage (underground) flow to the surface flow in computing total river flow— with implied criticism of the USBR for not doing so—for the purpose of maintaining a constant water surface but, strangely, does not subtract the seepage under the proposed concrete apron. Construction cost would be $2,700,000 plus the cost of recreational facilities and the improvement of the access road bringing the total cost to $3,000,000.

Gookin investigated several sources of possible finance: The Arizona Game and Fish Department, State Park Development, the Farmers Home Administration and the Bureau of Outdoor Rec-

---

20. Piping is a phenomenon whereby seepage through, under or around an earth dam or levee erodes the earth to create a "pipe" where the water can run at a great enough velocity to cause erosion and make the "pipe" larger. It often leads to failure.

21. Ski-jump spillways are common. Water flows down a concrete channel that is turned upward at its downstream end. The result is an arching jet of water that enters the river far enough downstream of the dam so that erosion near the dam does not occur.

reation under the Land and Water Conservation Program, and the Arizona Outdoor Recreation Coordinating Commission. Half of the Gookin report is devoted to the funding possibilities.

Council discussions

Many of the Wickenburg Town Council meetings over the next 15 months had the Box Canyon dam as an item for discussion. The Council voted to hire Gookin and Associates to make application to the Farmers Home Administration. Other funding sources were considered and applications were made. The last mention that I found in Town Council minutes was the reading of a letter from Arizona state representatives in Washington indicating their cooperation in obtaining funding. The entire project seems to have faded away without definite closure.

Postface

Failures sometimes occur for an obscure reason. The Tacoma Narrows Bridge collapsed in 1940. Bridge engineers of that era could hardly be blamed for not appreciating the destructive effect of aeroelastic flutter. Although cavitation was well known at the time of the design of Glen Canyon Dam, engineers would have had to be very perceptive to design the spillways against that destructive phenomenon. The reasons for the Walnut Grove Dam failure were not obscure. The mistakes in design and construction should have been obvious to engineers of the time.

Calculations

Any engineer reading this material will immediately ask "Where are the original calculations?" In my search I discovered few numbers and no calculations. Calculation is the thing engineers do! The late nineteenth century was a period of infrastructure construction: dams, railroads, bridges, tall buildings, water systems, sewerage systems. All of these required design engineers who could do the calculations.

Not one of the "engineers" employed by the Walnut Grove Water Storage Company seems to have computed the capacity of the spillway, not even the hydraulic consultant, Church. No one—with the exception of Wagoner—made even a rough guess at the amount of flood flow in the Hassayampa River, much less tried to calculate it. (Powell (page 123) does have a post-failure calculation in his congressional testimony and, although it is wildly wrong, a spillway designed to his calculated flow would have saved the dam.) The editor of *Engineering News* made some outrageous statements unsupported by calculations that he could have done.

Only a few of the calculations in this book could not have been done in the late nineteenth century. The determination of water levels downstream of the dam and after the flood had to await the theoretical development of the 1930s and subsequent application to stream flow in the 1950s. Engineering use of the numerical method and sufficient computing power did not develop until the 1960s. Also, those computations that are dependent on flow data could not have been done in 1890.

After failure, construction methods and the stability of the dam were questioned. Basic stability is a factor that could have been easily calculated. Questions about fundamental calculations do not appear in the interrogatories in the court trial. (Even lawyers should know better.)

Planning

Where are the plans? The Blake sketch in his diary hardly constitutes a plan and in any case is irrelevant due to the redesign by Robinson. The "Plans and Specification" of Appendix IV are extremely vague, giving only basic dimensions. The "Plans" say nothing of the spillway and other critical factors in the design of a dam. It seems that "the engineer in charge" was to build the dam on an ad-hoc basis.

Construction

Conflicting statements appear as to whether the dam rested on bedrock for its entire length or if part of it rested on the sand and gravel bed. The fact that such a question arises is damning in itself. The dam should not have rested on bedrock; it should have been *tied* into the bedrock. Moreover, the designers and builders apparently did not know the integrity of the rock under the dam or in the canyon walls.

The upstream and downstream slopes of the dam were steeper than the angle of repose for quarried rock (about 42 degrees). See the Schuyler quote on page 74. To depend on the facing to hold the rock in place would seem extremely unconservative and an invitation to failure even in the absence of overtopping.

Competence

The editor of *Engineering News* put the primary blame on the Walnut Grove Water Storage Company and on Van Beuren in particular. I would like to think that the engineers were not at fault, but certainly they shoulder a large portion of the blame. Of the two professional engineers (excluding Anderson, whose qualifications are unknown), Wagoner came out best due to his criticism of the dam before failure; however, he did not mention the primary cause of failure, the grossly inadequate spillway. Robinson had designed a much better spillway,

but still too small. That design and his firing after only four months on the job pretty much absolves him of blame. The other "engineers," including Brodie, did not appear to have the education or experience to do an adequate job. Perhaps the WGWSC is the primary culprit, although the Company was found not guilty in the trial. The lawyers did no better at obtaining justice than the "engineers" did in designing and building the dam.

Rebuilding

Rebuilding of the dam and the proposal to build a dam in Box Canyon appeared to be mostly an effort by well-meaning people to enhance the area around Wickenburg–Morristown–Wittmann. One name not mentioned previously is Garth Brown. He was a long-time Wickenburg resident who served as mayor and was on the Town Council for many years. "Brownie" promoted in every way he could the construction of a dam in Box Canyon in order to promote the Town. Although I greatly admire his unselfish dedication to the Town, both in this and in other matters, as a resident of Wickenburg I am glad that the Box Canyon effort failed.

Appendix I: Timeline

February 2, 1848—End of the American-Mexican war. Treaty of Guadalupe Hidalgo in which the United States acquired California, Nevada, Utah and parts of Colorado, Wyoming, New Mexico, and Arizona north of the Gila River.

September 9, 1850—Arizona included in the New Mexico Territory.

1853, 1854—The Gadsden Purchase whereby the United States acquired from Mexico the territory south of Gila River to the presentday boundary.

February 24, 1863—Arizona Territory created by U. S. Congress.

1863—Pauline Weaver led the Abraham Peeples party into central Arizona in search of gold. Rich Hill discovered. The Walker Party discovered gold near the present town of Walker, a few miles south of Prescott. Gold was discovered by Henry Wickenburg at the Vulture Mine and the Town of Wickenburg founded.

December 29, 1863—Arizona Territory formally organized at Navajo Springs, AT. John N. Goodwin was the first governor. (Note: John A. Gurley was appointed governor in March but died in August. Chief Justice Goodwin was appointed by President Lincoln to take his place.)

January 27, 1864—Temporary capital established at Fort Whipple in Little Chino Valley near Prescott.

May 18, 1864—Capital moved to Prescott.

September 26, 1864—Territorial Legislature (elected July 18) met for the first time and established the permanent capital at Prescott

October 24, 1864—The Territorial Legislature attempted, but failed, to move the Territorial Capital to Walnut Grove. The vote was eight in favor, nine opposed.

November 1, 1867—The Territorial Capital was moved to Tucson. June 24, 1874—The first post office was established at Walnut Grove. May 1, 1877—The Territorial Capital was returned to Prescott.

January 1881—Wells H. Bates and his brother DeWitt purchased the Marcus gold mine west of Rich Hill.

February 17, 1883—Bates established a mining claim and claimed all the water in the Hassayampa River. He selected a site on the Abner Wade ranch for a dam.

April 6, 1883—A U.S. Mineral Monument was erected at the junction of the Hassayampa and Fools Canyon.

April 7, 1883—Bates staked "Placer Claim No. 1" to be followed by 63 additional claims of 160 acres each.

1885—Bates convinced Charles H. Dillingham and J. N. Newberry to finance his project for hydraulic mining.

1885—The University of Arizona was established.

February 1886—William P. Blake was hired to examine the project.

May 5, 1886—The Walnut Grove Water Storage Company was incorporated.

June 1886—Bates was made president of the Piedmont Cattle Company. Bates was made director of the same company and the Walnut Grove Water Storage Company, which purchased Abner Wade's ranch.

August 1886—Blake and sons began surveying the site of the dam. December 1886—E. N. Robinson arrived at the dam site.

January 12, 1887—C. H. Dillingham, president of the Walnut Grove Water Storage Company, signed a contract with George D. Nagle and H. R. Leonard to build the Walnut Grove Dam. The contract stated that the work shall be carried out to the satisfaction of Colonel E. N. Robinson.

January 15, 1887—Blake was fired as chief engineer. Robinson assumed the position of chief engineer and superintendent. The dam had already reached a height of 30 feet.

April 1887—Robinson was fired. Nagel handled the construction for the following month without supervision from an engineer. Walter G. Bates became superintendent.

May 1887—Assistant Engineer (under Robinson) John M. Currier resigned.

August 10, 1887—Luther Wagoner took over as chief engineer, but (according to Brodie, 1890) was "given solely charge of the survey for a flume line 19 miles in length from the dam to Fools Creek." J. E. Anderson was placed in charge of construction of the dam.

Fall, 1887—Wagoner resigned. J. E. Anderson was appointed.

1887—Henry Spingler Van Beuren bought out the interest of Newberry in the Walnut Grove Water Storage Company.

Winter, 1887-1888—The dam and spillway were completed under Anderson and Walter Bates.

June 6, 1888—C. H. Dillingham resigned as president of the Walnut Grove Water Storage Company and became vice president.

1888—Alexander Oswald Brodie was appointed assistant engineer for the project.

September 1888—Work began on the Lower dam.

October 1888—Van Beuren became president of the Walnut Grove Water Storage Company.

1888—Brodie became chief engineer and superintendent after an absence from the project.

February 4, 1889—The Territorial Capital was moved to Phoenix.

March 1889—The reservoir spilled for the first time. The Lower dam, under construction, was destroyed.

May 31, 1889—The Johnstown flood.

December 1889—Wells Bates ordered an enlargement of the spillway and asked Benjamin S. Church to assess its adequacy.

Mid-February 1890—Work on the Lower dam was completed. Work continued on the flume from the Lower dam to the placer areas.

February 22, 1890, shortly after midnight—The dam collapsed. A primary player in the rescue efforts was Yavapai County Sheriff William O. ("Buckey") O'Neill.

February 1891—Trial in Maricopa County District Court involving 14 plaintiffs v. the Walnut Grove Water Storage Company.

October 31, 1891—Brodie was appointed receiver for the Walnut Grove Water Storage Company.

December 15, 1892—Brodie married Mary Hanlon. August 18, 1894—The Carey Act was signed into law.

1895—Blake established the Department of Geology at the University of Arizona.

April 1898—Brodie became Major of Volunteers in the Arizona squadron of Rough Riders. O'Neill was appointed captain of A Troop.

July 1, 1898—O'Neill was killed at San Juan, Cuba.

July 1, 1902—Brodie was appointed governor of the Territory of Arizona.

February 9, 1905—Brodie resigned as receiver for the Walnut Grove Water Storage Company and John Hanlon, his brother-in-law, was appointed.

February 14, 1905—Brodie resigned as governor. November 29, 1906—Henry S. Van Beuren died.

June 1908—Assets of the bankrupt Walnut Grove Water Storage Company were transferred to Eleanor Van Beuren Wittmann.

February 14, 1912—Arizona became the 48th state.

January 1, 1914—The Carey Act became effective in Arizona and Eleanor Van Beuren Wittmann filed for 17,500 acres of land near Morristown.

July 28, 1914—The United States entered World War I. December 23, 1917—Eleanor C. Van Beuren Wittmann died. November 11, 1918—World War I ended.

June 1923—The Nadaburg Irrigation District (later the Arizona Water Conservation District) was created.

1929—The name of the town of Nadaburg was changed to Wittmann.

October 24, 1929— "Black Tuesday," the stock market crash that led to the Great Depression

December 7, 1941—The United States entered World War II with the bombing of Pearl Harbor.

May 8, 1945— "V-E day" Germany surrendered. August 15, 1945— "V-J day" Japan surrendered.

February 1948—The U. S. Bureau of Reclamation issued its final report on the Box Canyon Dam and the Nadaburg Irrigation District ending the effort to build a dam in Box Canyon for the purpose of irrigation.

August 3, 1959—The Flood Control District of Maricopa County issued a comprehensive report on flood control projects. A dam in Box Canyon made the "not recommended" list.

May 23, 1968—The Wickenburg Town Council began an effort to obtain financing for a dam in Box Canyon for recreational purposes. Fifteen months later the effort faded away without closure.

Appendix II: Numbers

In this appendix I explain how I arrived at some of the data and calculations used elsewhere in the book. Amazingly, there are only a few numbers and even fewer calculations in the literature that I have consulted, even the engineering literature. Of course, the dam designers had little data in the late nineteenth century concerning watershed properties and flow. Apparently they did not utilize what data were available and made extremely unconservative assumptions about the river flow at the dam site. Although the calculations today are more sophisticated, many of the basic formulas were known in the 1890s. See for example Bowie (1885).

The calculations presented below are very approximate and may contain large errors. They are presented so that the reader can know how the numbers were obtained.

River flow

At or near the time of failure the water level in the lake had reached the top of the dam, 110 feet above the bed of the river, or higher. To calculate the river flow at that time, I consider the flow from the two twenty-inch outlet pipes, the flow over the spillway and the rate of rise of water in the reservoir. Conflicting dimensions are given in various publications; I use *Engineering News* (Oct. 20, 1888, p. 303).

Outlet pipes

When the water is at the top of the dam, the depth of the two 20-inch outlet pipes is 106 ft. The outflow would be approximately

$$Q_{pipes} = C_D A_{pipes} \sqrt{2gh} = (0.6)(4.36) \sqrt{2(32.2)(106)} = 216 \text{ cfs}$$

in which C_D is the coefficient of discharge, A_{pipes} is the area of the two pipes, g is the acceleration of gravity (32.2 ft/sec^2) and h is the depth of the pipes.

Spillway flow

The actual size of the spillway is a bit uncertain. *Engineering News* (Oct. 20, 1888, p. 303) shows it 20 ft wide by 5 ft deep. Schuyler (1901) says "The wasteway as built was 26 feet wide and 7 feet in depth ..." Brodie (see page 133) claims that he inherited a spillway 25 feet wide by 5 feet deep but began enlarging it and at the time of failure the "highest point [was] 8.10 feet below the crest of the dam [and it was] 31 feet wide at the narrowest part."[1] This statement is unclear if the narrowest point and the deepest point coincided, but I assume that they did and the flow is calculated based on a broad-crested weir (see, e.g., Roberson and Crow, 1993, eq. 15.18, p. 696),

$$Q_{spil} = 0.385 w C_{weir} h_{spil} \sqrt{2gh_{spil}}$$

$$= (0.385)(31)(1)(8.1) \sqrt{2(32.2)(8..1)} = 2208 \text{ cfs}$$

where w is the width and h_{spil} is the depth.

---

1. Measurements, made in October of 2007, confirm that the width of the spillway at the dam was 31 feet (see photo, Figure 5-10 on page 71). Due to sedimentation and erosion, we were unable to determine a definite depth.

Lake storage change

See the plot of lake elevation vs. storage below (Figure II-2 on page 130). When the water level was at the top of the dam, the reservoir area was approximately 1120 acres (48.8 million square feet). The elevation of the lake surface was increasing at 1.5 feet/hour according to witnesses and written accounts. Thus, the storage was increasing at the rate

$$Q_{stor} = \frac{dh}{dt} A_{res} \sqrt{2gh} = (1.5 / 3600)(48800000) = 20, 333 cfs$$

in which dh/dt is the rate of rise of the reservoir in ft/sec (ft/hr/3600 sec/hr) and A_{res} is the surface area of the reservoir in square feet.

Total flow and probability

The total flow in the river is sum of the flows from the outlet pipes, the spillway flow, and the rate of increase in storage in the reservoir—22,757 cfs[2]. The flow through the outlet pipes is well within the margin of error and is trivial. The spillway flow is small, almost an order of magnitude smaller than the total flow. How do these numbers compare to flood data taken later at various gages along the Hassayampa?

—Wagoner (page 18) estimated an ordinary flood at 10,000 cfs and a not-too-rare flood at 25,000 cfs.
—The 100-year flood at the Wagoner gage (page 19) is calculated to be 17,100 cfs by the Flood Control District of Maricopa County.
—The 100-year flood at the Box Canyon gage (page 19) is calculated to be 67,700 cfs by the Flood Control District of Maricopa County.

---

2. I have assumed that the reported rate of rise in the reservoir occurred while the spillway was discharging at capacity but before the dam was overtopped.

—The Box Canyon Dam spillway was designed for a maximum river flow of 183,000 cfs (Moritz, 1948, p. 139)

—In testimony before Congress, Powell (1892, p. 228) stated "... it was necessary to have a waste-weir which would discharge 6 acre-feet of water every second" or 261,360 cfs.

In the late 19th century, there was no data on flow in the Hassayampa River. The information the dam designers had available were (a) flood heights obtained from markings on the canyon walls, (b) observations of long-time residents and (c) rainfall records—the closest being at Fort Whipple, outside of the watershed—and very crude runoff calculations. I see no evidence that any such information was used in the design of the dam and its spillway.

What sort of probability should designers of such a project use? Modern-day flood flows through Wickenburg are calculated on the 100-year return period, as are insurance rates. The inundation limits of the 100-year flood are delineated on maps. However, a project with the destructive capability of Walnut Grove Dam should have a probability of failure in any one year considerably less than one percent, at least the 1000-year flood. Such structures are commonly designed for the "maximum probable flood."

The calculation of a one percent probability flow at the dam site is, of course, very approximate. My guess takes the 100-year flow at the Wagoner gage (17,100 cfs), divides it by the drainage area of 78 square miles (Table 1, page 19) and multiplies it by the watershed area of the dam site of 263 square miles to get a value of 57,658 cfs for the 100-year flow at the Walnut Grove Dam site. The river flow at the time of failure is calculated to be about the 20-year flood (see Table 2 on page 20).

Over the dam

It's interesting to compute the flow that was passing over the dam at the time of failure. The water level at the top of the dam was reportedly (*Engineering News*, Apr. 26, 1890, p. 390) three feet deep. Using the broad-crested weir formula for that depth and a width of 400 feet gives 6422 cfs—less than 40% of the flow in the river.

Flood Hydrographs

This section contains additional detail on the unsteady flow after the dam collapse and the calculations leading to hydrographs such as Figure 4-1. The simulation of the flood is done using the software HECRAS[3]. It solves the one-dimensional, unsteady flow equations for rivers under the assumption of hydrostatic pressure distribution. The basis for the calculation and the fundamental equations are found in Liggett (1994, pp. 298–305). The program requires input of the river geometry (slope and cross-sections), the boundary conditions (the upstream flow as a function of time and a condition at the downstream end, assumed in this case to be uniform flow), and the initial conditions (the flow and depth at the beginning of the simulation at each point in the river). Of these I have taken the downstream condition far from the areas of interest so that the assumption there has negligible effect. The initial conditions are obtained by running the simulation for a time before the period of interest.

The program also requires the input of an empirical friction coefficient (Manning's *n*) for each cross-section. The instantaneous

---

3. The program was written by the U.S. Army Corp of Engineers. The name comes from Hydrologic Engineering Center–River Analysis System.

flows and depths depend heavily on the choice of friction coefficient and even those experienced in river analysis have difficulty in determining the proper values. The best method is to run the program under known conditions and adjust the friction until the results match those conditions, a process called calibration.

Although river analysis is mathematical, the process has enough unknown factors to make it as much an art as a science. That is especially true on a river such as the Hassayampa where records are scarce and even more so in the simulation of extreme events where there is no record. Thus, these calculations must be considered highly approximate—an error of 25% could easily be present. Nevertheless, the results approximate to some degree the actual events of February 22, 1890.

Approximations
The following is a list of the approximations in the simulation of the flood.

- The geometry of the river—primarily the cross-sections— are assumed to be the same today (actually when the topo maps were made) as in 1890. In the Hassayampa River Canyon that assumption is probably of sufficient accuracy. In the vicinity of Wickenburg, it may be less accurate, due both to shifting sediment (sand) and construction on the riverbanks. I avoided, obviously, highly altered sections such as those at bridges.

- The tributaries are mostly ignored in the process. Their contribution in the extreme stages of the flow is relatively small and may actually be negative as flow is backed up.

- Seepage losses are ignored as they would be trivial, due to both the extreme flows and the fact that the ground was previously saturated.

- One hundred fifteen cross-sections were used (with additional interpolated sections), but the geometry is so complex that these may not be sufficiently representative in any location.

- Changes in the elevation of the riverbed—both during the flood and long-term changes since 1890—are unknown and have been ignored.

Dam Site Flow at Failure

Witnesses to the collapse said that the dam seemed to disintegrate almost instantly. Assuming instantaneous dam failure as though a giant had swept away the structure, critical flow would occur in the trapezoidal space where the dam stood. Critical depth in a trapezoidal channel is given by

$$g\left(wh_c + \frac{h^2}{2}\right)^3 = Q^2\left(w + 2\frac{h}{s}\right)$$

in which h_c is critical depth, g is the acceleration of gravity (32.2 ft/sec²), w is the base width of the trapezoid, Q is the flow rate and s is the slide slope (vertical/horizontal). The energy equation reduces to

$$h + \frac{V_c^2}{2g} = H$$

where V_c is critical velocity and H is the depth in the reservoir. Using the equations for flow and the area of a trapezoid,

$$Q = AV \quad A = wh_c + \frac{h_c^2}{s}$$

These relationships give four equations in hc, Q, Vc and A. The solution with H=110 ft, w=150 ft and s=0.88 is hc=80.7 ft, Q=846,900 cfs. That is, the instantaneous flow would have been more than 800,000 cfs, almost 15 times the 100-year flood. The depth of water at the dam site would have dropped to 80.7 feet with an average velocity in the cross-section of 43.4 feet per second.

Although this instantaneous flow would continue for a few seconds, the water level in the reservoir would be drawn down rapidly, causing a decrease in flow at the dam site and attenuation of the flood wave further downstream. The outflow is integrated over time and solved with the volume of the reservoir as a function of depth (Figure II-2) to provide a plot of flow vs time at the dam site.

Calibration

Five stream gages are now present on the Hassayampa below the Walnut Grove Dam site. They are Box Canyon, Wickenburg (the U.S. 60

bridge), Morristown, the bridge at the I-10 crossing and Arlington. Both the Wickenburg gage and the I-10 gage are located at bridge sections, which, of course, did not exist in 1890. The Arlington gage is far downstream and in a position that is not likely to yield good results. The Box Canyon and Morristown gages remain to determine the friction coefficient. These gages measure water depth and correlate flow with depth—a so-called rating curve. The accuracy of rating curves depends on the quality of data that were used to generate the curve, which in some cases may be quite poor. Moreover, most rating curves are not single valued in that the same flow rate leads to a different depth depending on whether the flow is increasing or decreasing.

To add to the difficulty, these rating curves extend to about 54,000 cfs of flow whereas the dam break flows were near 300,000 cfs at these locations. Though the roughness's probably changed little with the additional flow, that is definitely a source of error. Of course, some judgment went into choosing the roughness factors as descriptive tables and pictures of rivers of known roughness serve as a guide[4].

Calibration can also serve to nullify errors in geometry and other factors as those errors become absorbed in the roughness factor and tend to be canceled.

The Hydrograph

The water depths are more important than the flow in determining inundation. The flow is presented below as a matter of interest and as a comparison to other flows on the Hassayampa (Figure II-1).

Two "What Ifs?"

Perhaps the dam would not have failed if Robinson had been allowed to build the remote spillway. Or suppose that the culvert in the bottom of the dam had been operative.

---

4. For extensive tables see Chow (1959). Pictures are in Barnes (1967), available at http://wwwrcamnl.wr.usgs.gov/sws/fieldmethods/Indirects/nvalues/index.htm. Both are available in the program for steady, open-channel flow at http://cfd.mae.cornell.edu/~caughey/FluidMechSolns/.

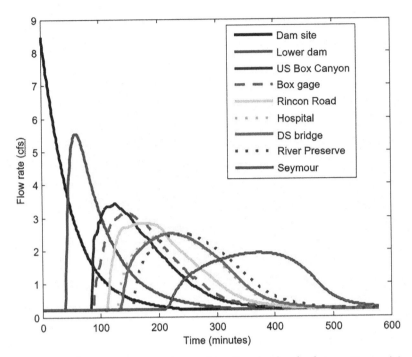

Figure II-1. Flow vs time at various points. For the depth plot see Figure 4-1.

Robinson's Spillway

E. N. Robinson had designed a spillway that was remote from the dam and of dimensions 55 feet by 12 feet (page 52). Speculation is that, if Robinson's spillway had been built, the dam would not have failed. Using the broad-crested weir formula with a depth of 12 feet and width of 55 feet gives a flow of 7064 cfs. That value added to the pipe flow gives a total of 7280 cfs that could have been passed down the river, about 38% of the river flow. Although a vast improvement— both in size and location—I believe that Robinson's spillway probably would not have saved the dam.

Flume flow

Engineering News (March 8, 1890, p. 229) speculates that had the gate blocking the flume been capable of being opened or been destroyed by dynamite, the dam may have been saved (page 65). The problem with calculating this "what if" is that the dimensions of the flume are not known for sure (page 63)[5]. Using

$$Q_{flume} = C_D A_{flume} \sqrt{2gh}$$

with CD=0.5 and h=110 gives

—3 by 4, *Qflume*=506 cfs
—3 by 5, *Qflume*=631 cfs
—5 by 5, *Qflume*=1052 cfs

Whichever of these numbers that you believe, it is small compared to the river flow. I disagree with *Engineering News*; opening of the flume could not have saved the dam.

Reservoir Area

The reported reservoir area has been 527.5 acres (Brodie letter, see page 131), 900 acres (Schuyler, *Engineering News*, Sept. 22, 1888, p. 232), 1000 acres (*Engineering News*, Mar. 1, 1890, p. 206) and 1100 acres (Walker, 1975, p. 78). Using USGS topo maps, I have obtained the reservoir area at approximately 980 acres when the water level stands at 100 feet above the stream bed (10 feet below the top of the dam) and 1170 acres

---

5. I think that the most probable the dimensions of the flume were 3 ft by 5 ft as the photographs in *Engineering News* (Oct. 10, 1888) show a nearly completed dam and in two of the photos the flume appears to be higher than it is wide. Also, Fig. III of the article shows a standing person who is slightly taller than the flume and considerably taller than the width of the flume. The discrepancy of dimensions may result because of double vertical walls that are evident in the photos. These walls were probably included to withstand the vertical load of the dam on the flume. The flow is assumed to take place between the innermost walls.

when the water level is at the top of the dam; see the plot below (Figure II-2).[6]

The calculation of reservoir area vs water level assumes that the river elevation in the vicinity of the dam site was the same when the topo map was made as it was 1890. I don't know if there has been accretion or erosion in the sand that makes up the riverbed. Even though such changes may displace the area-elevation curve, they would not materially affect the calculations of river flow.

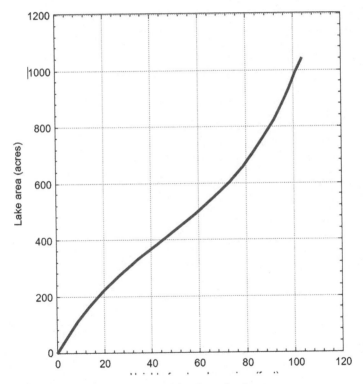

Figure II-2. Plot of reservoir area vs. depth at the dam

6. The plot was obtained assuming the streambed elevation at the dam was 3296.3 msl. The topo maps have a 40-foot contour interval. Each area was calculated for all contours up to 3400 feet, then a cubic spline was fitted to the points.

APPENDIX III:
BRODIE'S LETTER TO VAN BEUREN

The letter[1] from Brodie to Van Beuren, written after the dam collapse, is reproduced below. The letter has been retyped for readability, but I have endeavored to retain the original spelling and punctuation. The letter refers to an attached report by Assistant Superintendent Brown. I am unable to locate that attachment. Footnotes are my own opinions and interpretations.

COTTONWOOD CAMP, April 14th, 1890

H. S. VANBEUREN, *President Walnut Grove Water Storage Co.*

MY DEAR SIR:--On making my report on the severe disaster which overtook the Company's Works at Walnut Grove, on the morning of February 22d, it would perhaps be as well to give, as a preliminary, a general description of the dam and reservoir, with a general account of the methods of construction of the former.

---

1. I am indebted to Mr. Charles H. Herner, author of *The Arizona Rough Riders* and biographer of Alexander O. Brodie, for a copy of the letter. Mr. Herner lives in Tucson, Arizona. The letter appears as Appendix A in case number 1973, *Farmers Loan and Trust Company v. the Walnut Grove Water Storage Company.*

The reservoir covered an area of 527.5 acres[2] and received the drainage of about 500 square miles[3] of territory, mostly of a mountainous character, the greater part of which consisted of bare granite rock[4], allowing a quick flow of water resulting from melting snow and rainfall, to the receiving reservoir. The Dam, which closed the head of the Cañon and formed the reservoir, was of masonry and depended on the principle of gravity for its stability, was built straight across the cañon 110 feet high, 135 feet thick at base, 12 feet thick and 420 feet long on top, and was faced on the up-stream side with a skin consisting of two thicknesses of 3x8 plank firmly spiked to upright timbers 8x8, which were also firmly secured to cedar headers built in the wall.

Between the layers of plank was placed a layer of tarred felt paper, while the outside face of the skin was well caulked and covered with a thick coat of paraffin paint. The joints at the bottom and ends of the dam, where the same joined bedrock, were firmly closed by hydraulic cement mixed with sand in about the proportion of 3 to 1.

An off-set 12 ft. wide, where the works of the second engineer joined those of the first, was made in the dam, on which stood the wooden tower built of 8x8 halved in, making the tower 8 feet square, from the bottom of which were taken the discharge pipes, two of 20 inches diameter, each passing through a tunnel cut in solid rock, with gates at the lower end. There were

---

2. See the section on the reservoir area, page 129 (also see plot, Figure II-2).

3. Brodie's number for the drainage area is clearly too high. My own measurement gives 263 square miles (see page 17).

4. I am perplexed as to how Brodie characterizes the drainage area. Much of it is pine forest, some is grasslands and some desert growth such as paloverde, mesquite, greasewood and cactus. There is very little "bare granite rock." See footnote 5 on page 17.

two gates opening into the tower, lower at the 82-foot level, the other 20 feet above. These gates to be closed when it was found necessary to clean the pipes.[5] The outside walls of the dam were 12 feet thick and made of stone laid in place, while between these walls the space was filled with loose heavy rock.

The dam was started under Professor Wm. P. Blake as Chief Engineer and Superintendent for the Company, he holding this position and having general charge of the work from its inception in 1886 until about January, 1887, when a contract was let to Messrs. Nagle and Leonard of San Francisco to complete the dam, and Col. E. N. Robinson was placed in charge as Chief Engineer and Superintendent. During Prof. Blake's administration a wall was built across the cañon on the up-stream face of the dam, from bed-rock up to the creek bed and the skin placed thereon, the tunnel cut through the rock for discharge pipes, roads laid out and built, buildings constructed, and the works generally started.

Under Col. Robinson, who relieved Prof. Blake, the work was carried up to somewhere near the 40-foot level, lumber sawed and hauled and other necessary work done. Col. Robinson was relieved by the Company, I think in either May or June 1887, by Mr. Walter G. Bates as Superintendent, while Mr. J.

H. Bates, a former assistant under Col. Robinson, was retained for a short period as Chief Engineer. Upon the retirement of Mr. Jos. H. Bates[6], Mr. Luther Wagoner, C. E. was employed as

---

5. These gates simply controlled water entering the tower and were normally open. The pipe flow was controlled by valves near the downstream ends. The gates would have been inoperable unless the water level in the tower was close to the water level in the reservoir.

6. I can't find elsewhere a reference to J. H. or Jos. H. Bates. Perhaps Brodie had names and history confused.

Chief Engineer, but given solely charge of the survey for a flume line 19 miles in the length from the dam to Fools Creek.[7] Mr. J. E. Anderson being given more direct charge of the construction of the dam.

Upon completion the survey and maps, Mr. Wagoner left the Company's employ and returned to San Francisco. Mr. Walter Bates and Mr. Anderson remaining in charge until the completion of the dam and waste way, which occurred during the winter of '87 and '88. In cutting the waste way much of the rock taken therefrom was placed behind the dam, while afterwards 4,200 cars more of rock were added thereto as an additional safe guard.

In the fall of 1888 further work was projected by the Company and Mr. Anderson was sent down the cañon, 14 miles below the reservoir to construct a small service dam with a flume line 5 miles long to carry a head of 1,200 inches of water to the gravel deposits below. Mr. Anderson partly completed the excavation to bedrock at the dam site and the grade for the flume line when he retired and was relieved by myself the 31st July, 1889. The service dam was completed in December, '89, while the flume, with the exception of a few hundred feet was entirely built, when the flood, which wrecked the entire works, occurred.

This service dam was of the following dimensions, viz: 45 feet thick at the bottom, 44.5 feet high, 220 feet long and 10 feet wide at the top, covered on the up-stream side with a skin of two inch plank, tongued and grooved, well cemented at bottom

---

7. Apparently the original idea was to build a flume from the dam to the placer deposits. That idea was later abandoned in favor of the Lower dam that could divert water to a shorter (5-mile-long) flume.

and ends, making a perffectly [sic] water-tight dam, was built as an overflow dam with an overflow 80 feet long and 5 feet deep, sufficiently large for all purposes. This dam was severely tried before completion and stood the test well, water going entirely over twice at great depth and without moving a stone.

The flume, as constructed was 2.5x3.5 feet in the clear, with a grade of 8.5 feet to the mile, proper additions being made for curves carried water with a steady even flow, and was a tight flume in every sense of the word.

The waste way at the upper dam, as left by Messrs. Bates[8] and Anderson, was 25 feet wide by 5 feet in depth and extended around the west end of the dam. Deeming it advisable to be on the safe side, work was commenced on the 11th December to both widen and deepen this waste way, and also give a greater grade in order to materially increase the velocity of water flowing through. This work was carried on continuously until the day of the flood, at which time it was in the following shape, viz: the mouth funnel shaped, the very highest point being 8.10 feet below the crest of the dam, the fall being 1.67 feet in this funnel shaped mouth, increasing to 4.15 feet for the next 100 feet, and increasing visibly to the outlet, being 31 feet wide at the narrowest part, which was opposite the west end of the dam. This increase of size and grade had increased many-fold, the capacity of the waste way over the same as left by Messrs. Bates and Anderson, and as the former had carried, without trouble, the floods of the previous years, when the dam was so thoroughly tested, it was supposed, and naturally that the reconstructed

---

8. According to letter in the *Prescott Morning Courier* (Apr. 3, 1890) and *Engineering News* (Apr. 26, 1890, p. 389), Bates had been advocating for a larger spillway for some time before the failure.

one would prove adequate to any flood, and especially as storage room was always kept in the reservoir as a matter of precaution.

The flood, which resulted so disastrously for the Company and caused the breaking of the storage dam, on the morning of the 22d of February last, was one of unprecedented ferocity, as shown by the appearance of the river above the reservoir, where trees of from 25 to 50 years of age were torn up and carried down the stream by the force of the current, while all the forks of the main river were in the condition of flood. I have talked with many of the oldtime residents of this section of the Territory and the opinion of all seems to be the same, that the fall of water was unheard of, and that within the memory of man there never had been so general and heavy a rain resulting in such terrible floods.[9] Minnehaha Creek was, during the progress of and after the storm, a raging torrent, impassable to man or beast.

Before this latter flood the water in the reservoir had been drawn off until it required a rise of something over 18 feet in the lake for it to reach the top of the dam, which, when the area of the lake is considered, would give an immense storage room.

The break in the dam evidently occurred in the bottom and centre, as it was reported as nearly as could be judged, the break having taken place in the night, that it seemed to collapse all at once towards the centre, after the backing had been churned out by the whirlpool, caused by the meeting of the water going over the dam, and that coming through the waste way. The large amount going over the top for six hours before the break occurred and falling from such a height meeting that coming from the waste

---

9. The magnitude of the flood had a probability of 5% in any year according to the calculation shown on page 124.

way formed an eddy or whirlpool, the cutting power of which was simply irresistible,[10] and to this alone is due the breaking of the dam, the leak cutting no figure in the matter whatsoever, it being a general one at the ends and throughout the whole structure. During the entire time of the flood the waste way was clear and open and both discharging pipes flowing a full head.

A waste way was proposed, I believe by Col. Robinson, which would have consisted of a tunnel leading from the reservoir to Cottonwood Creek which, should it ever have been cut through and become clogged during the progress of a freshet, would have been defective, as it would allow of no way of being cleared.[11]

The storage dam was thoroughly tested during the floods of the preceding year, at which time the water came to within 16 inches of the top and its stability was thoroughly believed in by both yourself and myself, as we were perfectly willing to live on the river below and so without fear of a disaster above.

Attention is invited to the report of Mr. Brown, in charge of the work at the upper dam, hereto attached marked "A", in which he gives an account of the flood and the consequent breaking of the dam, which coming as it did during the night, was the cause of great loss of life and property at the lower camps. Mr. Brown sent a messenger to warn those at these points of danger, giving

---

10. I am perplexed as to why Brodie, or the other engineers, did not realize that ending the spillway at the toe of the dam was flirting with disaster.

11. I doubt that Robinson proposed a tunnel as this is the only reference to a tunnel that I have found. In fact, there is a saddle in the terrain between the reservoir and Cottonwood Creek so that a tunnel would be unnecessary. Further, Brodie's remarks on Robinson's spillway being defective are invalid if for no other reason that exclusion devices such as trash racks and skimmers could have kept it from being plugged. See page 52 for more information.

him the best horse to be had, but the man sent being addicted to strong drink, was unable to pass a grog shop on the road without partaking of liquor and taking some with him. On becoming incapacitated he turned back, leaving the unfortunates below to their fate. A later messenger also failed to get through in time. It seems strange that a man should be so devoid of the feelings of humanity as to fail when sent on such an errand of mercy.

It was found that the law would fail to reach this man Burke and punish him for his criminal negligence.

Mr. Brown had orders from me, on the least approach of danger, to send messengers warning the people below, in order that they might be up, dressed, on the lookout and have most of their valuables saved.

It is unnecessary to speculate on the result of Burke, the messenger's failure to get through. In this case however the people should have been sufficiently warned by the rise in the river, which, after the water started through the waste way above, came up to some of their tents and they should not have allowed themselves to go to sleep until all danger was passed. In one case in particular—that of Boone, who had a family there, and who rather than take warning and move, dug ditches around his tent to keep the water out.—Only a piece of perfect folly would send people to sleep after a three days' steady rain, common prudence should keep them awake.[12]

---

12. Brodie seems a bit disingenuous. He states above that "we [he and Van Beuren] were perfectly willing to live on the river below ... without fear of a disaster above" but then gave an order to Brown to send a warning "on the least approach of danger" and in this paragraph appears to blame the victims for their own deaths.

Great damage was done by this breaking of the reservoir dam, the river bed being ground sluiced through the cañon as far as the lower camp at Cottonwood, at which point the bottom widens out, not a tree being left in that distance, while the lower dam was entirely obliterated, not a vestige of it being left and about a mile and a quarter of the flume carried off. The lake must have moved almost as a solid body, as the main river passed from the cañon, 18 miles as near as can be calculated, in the incredibly short space of time of 45 minutes; this allowing the unfortunate people only seconds in which to save themselves. The only parts of the upper or storage dam left consists of a small shoulder of masonry at the upper part of each end, while a small part of the foundation still stands at each side of the creek, showing conclusively that the dam went out first in the centre.

Many notices and criticisms on the construction of the upper dam have from time to time appeared in public prints, as well as theories accounting for the disaster, emanating from the pens of engineers, whom it is very reasonable to suppose, never saw either of the dams, at least their presence in the camps has never been known.

It is hard to judge of the construction of dams from the outside, and after the work has been completed, the riverbed being covered with sand and water. As cheap notoriety may however be gained by such criticisms, no matter how far from correct.

Some have spoken of a downstream curve in the upper dam. Very few men have ever seen rough masonry such as the dam was constructed of, settle exactly straight, and in the present case the dam had the appearance of a greater sag than it really had, due to the inaccuracy shown in putting on the outside skin.

Upon the news of the disaster reaching Prescott, the people of that town responded generously and freely to relieve the suffering, while too much praise cannot be awarded to Adjutant-General W. O. O'Neill for his promptness in proceeding to scene of the wreck, rendering assistance to the living, and recovering and burying the dead, being ably assisted in this work by Messrs. Redington, Brown and Lansing in the Company's employ, and Mr. Robert Brown the resident merchant. Yavapai County has paid, by action of the Board of Supervisors, something like $1,600 expended in aid of the destitute survivors of the flood, while the Company has done all that lay in its power to alleviate the suffering.

The breaking of the upper dam and the consequent wrecking of the Company's works by the rushing of nearly 5 billion gallons of water down the cañon, was peculiarly unfortunate just at the time it happened, as the flume was very nearly completed, the Hydraulic plant purchased and in Phoenix, so that in a very short time all of the carpenters and others would have been out of the cañon and in a place of safety, and therefore no lives lost; the Company would have known the exact value of the bars from a working test, and whether it would pay to re-build, taking into consideration the mining proposition only. As an irrigation scheme its value is easily determinable, the amount of water it being possible to draw from the reservoir for such a purpose being very nearly known.

The Walnut Grove Water Storage Company has at least thoroughly demonstrated the fact that there is plenty of rainfall in Arizona, if the same can only be stored to irrigate the greater part of the valleys and plains suitable for the farmer and fruit raiser.

Upon the successful solution of the water storage problem in a country subject to such heavy floods depends the future prosperity of the territory.

Attached hereto marked "B" will be found the amount of rainfall in Prescott during the months of December, January, and February, as reported from the Signal Office at Whipple Barracks.

Trusting that the above report gives all the data that you may require, and will therefore prove satisfactory, I am, sir,

Very respectfully your obedient servant,

(Signed)

ALEX. O. BRODIE

Chief Eng. and Supt. W. G. W. S. Co.

APPENDIX IV:
PLANS AND SPECIFICATIONS

The contract between Dillingham, as president of the Walnut Grove Water Storage Company, and the contracting firm of Nagel and Leonard was signed on January 12, 1887. The "Plans and specifications" for the dam are attached to that contract. This material is available in the Arizona State Libraries, Archives and Public Records as a part of the trial of *Wickenburg et al. v. the Walnut Grove Water Storage Company*.

The plans and specifications are extremely brief for such a complex endeavor. The decisions are left to the "engineer in charge." The basic dimensions of the dam appear in sketch form. Sketch A is not shown herein; it simply pictures a cross-section of the dam with only a few dimensions. The below mentioned diagrams 'B' and 'C' do not appear in the court record. Neither the agreement nor the plans refer to the spillway.

PLANS AND SPECIFICATIONS

For a stone dam to be built in Hassayampa River, Yavapai County, Arizona Territory, on what is known as Wade's Ranch, about fifty miles south of Prescott by the traveled road.

Said dam will be about 110 feet high, 330 feet long on top, and will have a width on top of about 10 feet, and a slope of about 56 degrees on the lower side, and about 62 degrees on the upper side, to the base.

The entire cubical contents of the said dam to be composed of rock of such sizes and shape as can be quarried from the adjacent walls of the canyon. The quantity of material in said dam is estimated at 45,000 cubic yards, more or less.

The walls of the upper and lower slopes (before named) are to be properly laid up with the largest stone that can be secured from the adjacent quarries, said stone to be laid into dry rough masonry, and as directed by the engineer in charge.

The lower wall to have a width of 15 feet at its base and to be at least 9 feet wide at the 100-foot level, as shown in the following diagram, marked 'A'.

The upper wall, upon which the apron or skin is to rest shall be at least 12 feet wide at its base, and at least 6 feet at the 100-foot line, as shown in the foregoing diagram, marked 'B'.

Both of these walls shall be laid in a substantial and workmanlike manner, and as directed by the engineer in charge of said work.

The filling of stone between the said upper and lower walls (see diagram, 'C') shall be free of earth and sand except in such places as may be designated by the engineer in charge.

The stone comprising such filling to be of such dimensions as can be obtained from the adjacent quarries
after the largest stones are selected therefrom for use
in the upper and lower walls in said dam, as herein-
before stated and shown in the diagram, marked 'A'
and 'B'.

The coping of said dam shall be of as large stone as
can, in the judgment of the engineer in charge, be
conveniently obtained from the adjacent quarries.
The up-stream side of the dam and wall 'B' (see diagram) is to be covered with three-inch plank, spiked
to upright or horizontal timbers, placed as directed
by the engineer in charge.

The spikes shall be of such dimensions and character
as may be designated by the engineer.

The Company are [sic] to furnish the pipes that are
to pass from the water tower through the dam, and
the contractor is to put the same in place and securely
cover it with stone, as directed by the engineer.

Any cement that may be required for covering said
pipes shall be furnished by the company free of cost
to the contractor.

The connection of pipe to the tower and discharge
gates shall be made by the Company.

REFERENCES

Anon., "A narrative history of the Hassayampa River project in Arizona, 1882 to 1936," published in the *Wickenburg Sun*, May 1, 1936.

Bansner, Jeannie, "Jeannie's jottings from downstairs," *Buckaroo*, Volunteer Newsletter, Desert Caballeros Western Museum, Wickenburg, Arizona, November 2006, p. 2.

Barnes, Harry H., Jr., *Roughness Characteristics of Natural Channels*,

U. S. Geological Survey, Government Printing Office, 1967.

Barnes, Will C., *Arizona Place Names*, The University of Arizona Press, Tucson, 1988.

Bates, Walter Gillette, "Water-Storage in the West," *Scribner's Magazine*, Vol. VII, No. 1, January 1890.

Blake, William P., "Note upon some results of the storage of water in Arizona," *Transactions of the American Institute of Mining Engineers*, 1889, pp. 476–478.

Bowie, Augustus, *A Practical Treatise on Hydraulic Mining in California*, D. Van Nostrand, New York, 1885.

Brodie, Alexander O., Letter reporting on the failure of the Walnut Grove Dam to H. S. Van Beuren, Apr. 14, 1890.

Buchanan, Scott, "RoadRunner Prospectors' Club Newsletter," Vol. 20, No. 7, July 2006, pp. 6–8; see also "Floods Happen! A Publication of the Arizona Floodplain Management Association," Vol. 23, No. 1, Spring 2006, pp. 8–12.

Burden, Dana W., *Desert Hiking Out Wickenburg Way*, Pathfinder Publishing, Wickenburg, Arizona, 2004.

Burden, Dana, and Joe Stevens, *Where the Past Lives—Constellation Road*, Pathfinder Publishing, Wickenburg, Arizona, 2006.

Burden, Kate, "The Hassayampa River," *Arizona Highways*, May 1956, Vol. XXXII, No. 5, pp. 34–37.

Byrkit, James W. and Bruce Hooper, *The Story of Pauline Weaver: Arizona's Foremost Mountain Man, Trapper, Gold-Seeker, Scout, Pioneer*, Sierra Azul Productions, 1993.

Chow, Ven-Te, *Open-Channel Hydraulics*, McGraw-Hill, 1959.

Conner, Daniel Ellis, *Joseph Reddeford Walker and the Arizona Adventure*, edited by Donald J. Berthrong and Odessa Davenport, University of Oklahoma Press, 1956.

Corbusier, William T., *Verde to San Carlos: Recollections of a Famous Army Surgeon and His Observant Family on the Western Frontier, 1869-1886*, D. S. King, publisher, 1969.

Corle, Edwin, *The Gila, River of the Southwest*, University of Nebraska Press, 1951.

Costa, John E., "Floods from dam failures," *Flood Geomorphology*, edited by Victor R. Baker, R. Craig Kochel and Peter C. Patton, John Wiley and Sons, New York, 1988.

Costa, J.E. and J. E. O'Connor, "Geomorphically effective floods," *Natural and Anthropogenic Influences in Fluvial Geomorphology, Geophysical Monograph*, vol. 89, 1995, pp. 45–56.

Dill, David B., Jr., "Terror on the Hassayampa—The Walnut Grove Dam Disaster of 1890," *Journal of Arizona History*, 1987, pp. 283–306.

Dill, David B., Jr., "William Phipps Blake: Yankee gentleman and pioneer geologist of the far West," *Journal of Arizona History*, 1991 32(4), pp. 385–412.

Durrenberger, Robert W., and Robert S. Ingram, *Major Storms and Floods in Arizona 1862–1977*, Office of the State Climatologist, Climatological Publications, Precipitation Series No. 4, 1978.

Dutton, C., Congressional Committee on Irrigation and Reclamation of Arid Lands, Washington, March 13, 1890.

Ely, Lisa L., "Response of extreme floods in the southwestern United States to climatic variations in the late Holocene," *Geomorphology*, vol. 19, 1997, pp. 175-201.

Flood Control District of Maricopa County, "Comprehensive flood control program report," 1963.

Gilbert, Bil, *Westering Man*, Atheneum, New York, 1983.

Granger, Byrd Howell, *Arizona's Names, Historical Names of Places in Arizona*, The Falconer Publishing Company, Tucson, 1983.

James, George Wharton, *Arizona, the Wonderland*, The Page Company, Boston, 1917.

Keithley, Ralph, *Buckey O'Neill*, The Caxton Printers, Ltd., Caldwell, Idaho, 1949.

Kochel, R. Craig, "Geomorphic impact of large floods: review and new perspectives on magnitude and frequency," *Flood Geomorphology*, edited by Victor R. Baker, R. Craig Kochel and Peter C. Patton, John Wiley and Sons, New York, 1988.

Liggett, James A., *Fluid Mechanics*, McGraw-Hill, 1994.

Lloyd, Elwood, *Arizonology*, The Coconino Sun, Flagstaff, 1933.

Maass, John, "Who invented Dewey's classification," *Wilson Library Bulletin*, Vol. 47, No. 4, December 1972, pp. 335–341.

Mahoney, Ralph, *Arizona Days and Ways Magazine*, Feb. 17, 1957.

Moritz, E. A., "Hassayampa project, Arizona: project planning report no. 3-8b.1-0," Preliminary Report, United States Bureau of Reclamation, Sept. 1945 (2 vols).

Moritz, E. A., "Hassayampa project, Arizona: project planning report no. 3-8b.1-2," United States Bureau of Reclamation, Feb. 1948.

Osterkamp, W. R., and J. E. Costa, "Changes accompanying an extraordinary flood on a sand-bed stream," in *Catastrophic Flooding* (L. Mayer and D. Nash, eds.), Allen and Unwin, Boston, 1987.

Pope, G. L., P. D. Rigas, and C.F. Smith, "Statistical Summaries of Streamflow Data and Characteristics of Drainage Basins for Selected Steamflow-Gaging Stations in Arizona Through Water Year 1996,"

U.S. Department of the Interior, U.S. Geological Survey, Tucson, Arizona, 1998.

Powell, John Wesley, *U. S. Geological Survey Eleventh Annual Report* (available as U.S Congressional Serial Set, Vol. No. 2844, Session Vol. No. 15, 51st Congress, 2nd Session, H. Exec. Doc. 1 pt. 5 vol. 4 pt. 2), 1892.

Raymond, Rossiter W., "Memoir of William Phipps Blake," *Geological Society of America Bulletin*, Pittsburgh meeting, pp. 36–47.

Roberson, John A., and Clayton T. Crowe, *Engineering Fluid Mechanics*, Houghton Mifflin Company, 1993.

Robinson, William Henry, *The Story of Arizona*, The Berryhill, Company, Phoenix, 1919.

Roeske, R. H., M. E. Cooley, and B. N. Aldridge, "Floods of September 1970 in Arizona, Utah, Colorado, and New Mexico," USGS Water Supply Paper 2052, 1978.

Schuyler, James D., *Reservoirs for Irrigation, Water-Power, and Domestic Water-Supply*, Wiley, New York, 1901.

Schuyler, James Dix, *Reservoirs for Irrigation, Water-Power, and Domestic Water-Supply*, Second edition, Wiley, New York, 1909.

Stromberg, J. C., B. D. Richter, D. T. Patten and L. G. Wolden, "Response of a Sonoran riparian forest to a 10-year return flood," *Great Basin Naturalist*, 53(2), 1993.

Stromberg, Juliet C., Jana Fry and Duncan T. Patten, "Marsh development after floods in an alluvial, arid-land river," *Wetlands*, Vol. 17, No. 2, June 1997.

Trimble, Marshall, *Roadside History of Arizona*, Mountain Press Pub. Co., Missoula, MT, 2004.

Wagoner, Luther, "Notes on the Walnut Grove Dam," *Transactions, Technical Society of the Pacific Coast*, Vol. 5, Oct. 1888.

Wagoner, Luther, and William Henry Heuer, "San Francisco Harbor Its Commerce and Docks with Complete Plan for Development Being the Report of the Engineers of the Federated Harbor Improvement Association," 1908.

Walker, Dale L., *Buckey O'Neill: The Story of a Rough Rider*, The University of Arizona Press, Tucson, 1975.

Washington Letter, *Journal of the American Geographical Society of New York*, Vol. 22, 1890, p. 155. (Statement by Lieut. Glassford of the Signal Corps.)

Webb, Robert H., Stanley A. Leake, and Raymond M. Turner, *The Ribbon of Green: Change in Riparian Vegetation in the Southwestern United States*, The University of Arizona Press, Tucson, 2007.

Willson, Roscoe, G., "State's worst disaster wipes out work camp,"

Arizona Days and Ways, Oct. 2, 1949.

Willson, Roscoe, G., "Did whisky cause the great disaster?" *Arizona Days with Roscoe Willson*, Mar. 21, 1965.

Wilson, H. M., *American Irrigation Engineering*, (also "Thirteenth annual report of the U. S. Geological Survey," *U. S. Congressional Series Set*, Vol. No. 3092, Session Vol. No.17, 52nd Congress, 2nd Session), 1893, pp. 297–301.

INDEX